Simple Working Models of Historic Machines

(easily made by the reader)

Aubrey F. Burstall

THE M.I.T. PRESS
Massachusetts Institute of Technology
Cambridge, Massachusetts

Preface

This book is intended for all those who like to experiment and make things work, from the schoolboy upwards. It will help them to experience the pleasure and satisfaction of making things with their own hands.

Simple instructions are given for making and putting to work models of scientific and historic significance, while suggesting their place in the advance of technical progress through the ages.

What is visualized here is not model making as ordinarily understood, for the devices described do not require for their making very much skill or craftsmanship. Thus few detailed drawings—in the engineering sense—have been included because the object in mind is to encourage a talent for experimenting and improvisation.

Given the materials and facilities, and a modicum of supervision, the schoolboy who is really interested can persuade his hands to make for him whatever he wants to make, as is often evident in the elaborate project work undertaken in some school subjects. Like primitive man, he usually has that invaluable asset—plenty of time to try things out.

If there is a school workshop, with a tradesman/technician in charge, the latter must try to suppress his innate desire for perfection and accurate workmanship when the rough models of medieval times are in question: a sapling cannot be measured in thousandths of an inch.

During the last fifteen years—1952–67, working models of all these machines of historic interest have been made to my design in our workshops in the department of Mechanical Engineering at the University of Newcastle upon Tyne. They were intended primarily to illustrate important events in the history of mechanical engineering and secondly to bring the reality of these events to first-year students attending the course. Much appeared to be learned by feeling and touching a working model that otherwise eluded them when only diagrams, slides, or cinema films were used.

These working models have been shown to schoolboys, ages twelve to eighteen, on many occasions. Various types of school have been visited, when as many models as I could conveniently pack into my car were set to work. The opportunity of operating the models for themselves always created great enthusiasm, and certainly tested the durability of the apparatus.

In 1965 the models were grouped to form the basis of the three annual Holmes Memorial Lectures at the University of Newcastle, with practical demonstrations on a suitable scale to appeal to the wider audience.

My sincere thanks are due to those members of the staff of the Department of Mechanical Engineering who have helped me in the design and construction of these models, all of which were made and tried out in the departmental workshop. I am particularly grateful to the technicians, from the chief technician downwards. They gave me their enthusiastic support during the many trials and modifications that were needed to make the constructions as simple and effective as possible.

Finally, I am much indebted to Mr Peter Elliot, Senior Technician, who made all the scale drawings in this book and contributed many useful suggestions including the use of proportional dividers by the reader for making the models in accordance with the drawings.

A.F.B.

Acknowledgments

Certain illustrations in this book have been borrowed from other publications, and the following list gives the sources from which they have been taken. Permission for the reproduction of any copyright material is gratefully acknowledged by author and publisher.

These References form a useful list for further reading.

Page	Source
12	*Report of the Smithsonian Institution*, 1894, p. 721.
13 (*bottom*)	W. L. Goodman, *A History of Woodworking Tools*. London, G. Bell & Sons Ltd., 1964.

14   *Report of the Smithsonian Institution*, 1894, p. 735.

17 (*bottom*)   Photograph kindly lent by Mr. W. L. Goodman.

18   C. Singer et al. (Ed.), *A History of Technology*, Vol. II. Oxford, Clarendon Press, 1956. (By courtesy of *Endeavour*.)

20   R. S. Woodbury, *A History of the Lathe to 1850*. Monograph of the Society for the History of Technology. Cambridge, Mass., M.I.T. Press, 1961.

22 (*left*), 78   I. B. Hart, *The Great Engineers*. London, Methuen & Co. Ltd., 1928.

28   A. Young, *A Six Months' Tour through the North of England*, Vol. II, 1770. (Reproduced in *A History of the Iron and Steel Industry* by H. R. Schubert. London, Routledge & Kegan Paul Ltd., 1957.)

30, 44   J. Needham and W. Ling, *Science and Civilization in China*, Vol. IV. Cambridge University Press, 1965.

40, 58, 62   F. Klemm, *Technik: Eine Geschichte ihrer Probleme*. Freiburg/München, Verlag Karl Alber, 1954. (English translation: *A History of Western Technology* by D. Singer. London, George Allen & Unwin Ltd., 1959.)

42   Unknown source. (Reproduced in *A History of Technology*, Vol. I, ed. by C. Singer et al.)

48 (*top*), 76   A. F. Burstall, *A History of Mechanical Engineering*. London, Faber & Faber Ltd., 1963. (From Hero's *Pneumatics*.)

60   C. G. de Montauzon, *La science et l'art de l'ingénieur aux premiers siècles de l'empire romain*. Paris, Ernest Leroux Éditeur, 1909.

64   Hoover (Ed.), Agricola's *De Re Metallica*. New York, Dover Publications Inc., 1950.

66 (*left*)   S. Shapiro, 'The Origin of the Suction Pump', *Technology and Culture*, Vol. V, No. 4, 1964. Chicago, Ill., University of Chicago Press.

73 (*bottom*)   C. Singer et al. (Ed.), *A History of Technology*, Vol. I. Oxford, Clarendon Press, 1954. (By courtesy of *Endeavour*.)

Contents

Chapter I   Materials and Tools for making Working Models of Machines

Basic Equipment. The first essential is a workshop or working space which should be as large as possible. It needs to be well lighted, preferably to have a wooden floor, a radiator of some kind to maintain a reasonable working temperature in cold weather, electric power points and if possible a water tap and sink, although these last need not necessarily be in the same room as the workshop. Clearly the workshop needs a work bench, preferably made of wood, on which hammering can be done, and with a vice fitted at one end. The bench should be not less than about 4 ft long by 2 ft wide and at the most convenient height for working.

It is important that the bench should be near the source of light, natural or artificial. The most essential attachment to the bench is the vice which should be placed at one end, well supported with a heavy leg beneath so that hammering can be done on it. Heavy hammering should, of course, be done on an anvil or piece of heavy metal, separate from the bench and conveniently mounted in a section of a tree-trunk resting on the floor. Sufficient storage space for the materials of construction that are going to be used in making the models, particularly steel, copper, brass, timber and plastic materials, will be needed. Some can be stored in racks or bins, or open-topped boxes, while small articles such as screws, washers, etc. can be most conveniently kept in the plastic boxes on sale quite cheaply at multiple stores. Hand tools need to be stored on hooks or shadow boards within easy reach of where the operator is working.

In addition to the work bench, it is desirable to have some table and shelf space where the finished and partly constructed models can be erected and tried out. Cupboard space should be available somewhere—not necessarily in the workshop—where the finished models can be stood, out of the dust, when not in use.

The tools required by the amateur for making these models may conveniently be divided into a number of groups. It is not proposed to list every tool that is required since some individual preference may be exercised among the wide variety that is available today. The tools in the first group are holding devices, among these are vices—the bench vice and the hand vice—pincers, pliers, shifting spanners, screwdrivers, screw-clamps and footprints. The second group can be described as cutting and deforming tools and includes hammers, a mallet, cold-chisels, punches, tin-snips, files, hacksaws, both hand drill and breast drill and, of course, a set of twist drills and a pair of scissors. The third group consists of sharpening equipment which includes emery wheel, carborundum stone, oil-stone and emery paper. In the fourth group are the measuring and marking tools, including rules, steel tape-measures, scribers, dividers, feeler gauges, centre punches, squares and protractors. The fifth group comprises joining materials and includes a soldering kit, adhesives of various kinds such as Araldite, Evostick, and various cements, including rubber solution. The last group includes a useful range of woodworking tools such as saws, chisels, rasps, Surform, plane, bradawl, gimlet, drills and sandpaper.

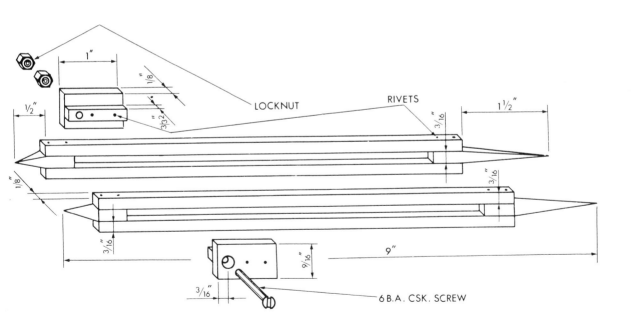

Fig. 1/1   Details of proportional dividers

Proportional Dividers. Sufficient detail has been given for each of the models in the perspective drawings (which are to scale) to enable anyone to make them by scaling off dimensions in any of the three planes, namely, up and down, sideways, and front and back. The quickest way of doing this is by means of a pair of proportional dividers, Fig. 1/1.

The construction of the dividers can be seen from the drawing where the necessity for machining parallel surfaces has been avoided by using square-section sides of metal, preferably steel with a brass block sliding between. The points at either end of the dividers should preferably be made of steel and can be shaped by filing from square material.

To use the dividers the scale in inches marked on every model drawing must be used and the distance between the two points at one end of the dividers set to say 6 in on the vertical scale, then the fulcrum of the dividers is adjusted until the distance between the two points at the other end of the dividers is 6 in. The fulcrum can then be adjusted for tightness and the real lengths in the vertical direction of any part of the model can be determined by placing the two points on the right-hand side of Fig. 1/2 against the vertical distance on the drawing of any line it is desired to measure, when the distance between the points at the left-hand side will be the actual vertical distance in question on the model. A similar procedure can be followed with regard to the other two lines on the scale in inches, marked on each of the drawings. It should be noted that once the fulcrum has been tightened for the vertical position, the same setting applies to each of the other planes shown on the scale in inches, though measurement made at intermediate angles will not be correct if they are scaled in the same way.

Drawings. Most of the drawings in this book are isometric though a few are oblique. Isometric sketches such as Fig. 2/1 are generally considered to give a representation that is more easily appreciated by the beginner than the normal engineering drawings showing plan, elevation and side view which are known as orthogonal projections. In a few cases, e.g. Figs. 2/8, 3/5, 4/1, 5/3, orthogonal projections have been given because all the necessary details of these models could not be conveniently represented in isometric drawings.

Improvised Equipment. A great many other tools that are available might have been suggested but in the writer's view, they are not essential. For instance, sets of taps and dies are nice things to have but their purchase can hardly be justified for this sort of work when bolts, nuts and screws can be obtained so easily and cheaply without having to make them for oneself. There are other tools which though not essential would be a great convenience and would speed up the making of many of the models. Chief among these is the portable electric drill with its various attachments for sawing, grinding, and so on.

It will be noticed that in many cases household utensils and articles of commerce that can be purchased from the ironmongers have been used instead of making parts specially for the models. Thus plastic buckets and transparent plastic boxes have been freely used—sometimes modified by drilling or cementing the lids on to make them airtight. Likewise, broom-shanks and coffee-table legs with screwed ends have been found to have uses other than those originally intended.

The reader will find that to use his ingenuity in this way—by adapting finished or partly finished parts to his particular uses, is in itself a rewarding challenge which often saves a great deal of time—and sometimes money as well.

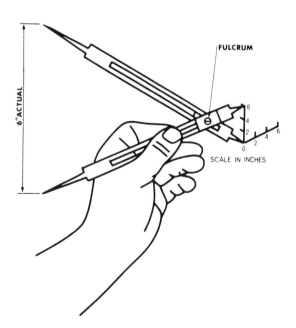

Fig. 1/2   Use of proportional dividers

Chapter II   Some Ancient Machine Tools

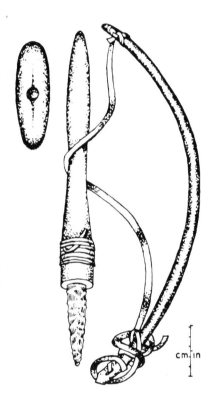

Bow drill from Alaska with flint bit and socket for upper end of shaft.

Bow Drill

Most modern machine tools owe their origins to the bow drill, Fig. 2/1, which has been in use since prehistoric times.

It can be made very simply and easily and consists essentially of four parts:

1 A bent stave about 3 ft 6 in long of green wood with a strong string or piece of blind cord joining its two ends.
2 A round drill shaft about 4 in long and $\frac{3}{4}$ in diameter which has the bow cord wrapped around it.
3 A drilling bit made of stone or metal forced into the lower end of the drill shaft and
4 A palm piece made of stone or wood which is held in the palm of the left hand and serves as a support and bearing for the upper end of the drill shaft.

Drilling is done by holding the drill shaft vertically with the palm piece in the left hand and drawing the bow backwards and forwards whereupon the drilling shaft and drill are rotated alternately clockwise and anti-clockwise, while the bow maintains sufficient tension in the cord to provide enough friction between the cord and the drill shaft to prevent slipping; thus the drill shaft is rotated. Sufficient downward pressure must be maintained on the drill by the palm piece to force the drill down into the work. The palm piece should have a hole or socket into which the upper end of the drill shaft enters. The drilling bit needs to be sharpened from time to time whether it is stone or metal so that a cutting edge is maintained. The drill bit is flattened into a batswing shape. (Twist drills of the type used today in rotary drilling machines were invented about a hundred years ago.)

In the bow drill, the backwards and forwards reciprocating motion of the hand is converted into clockwise and anti-clockwise rotary motion of the drill head.

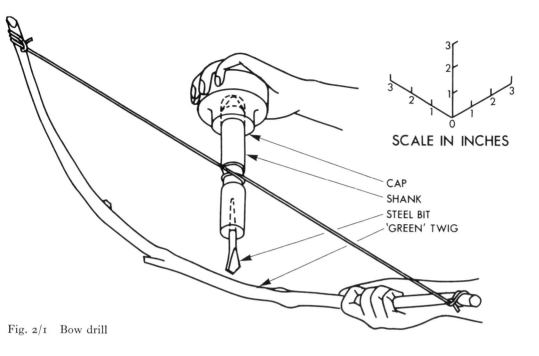

CAP
SHANK
STEEL BIT
'GREEN' TWIG

SCALE IN INCHES

3 2 1 1 2 3
3 2 1 0 1 2 3

Fig. 2/1   Bow drill

Egyptian cabinet-makers.   Mastaba of Tiye, Saqqara, 2540 B.C.

Pump Drill

Closely related to the bow drill—for it has the same component parts—is the pump drill, Fig. 2/2, in which a hole has been made in the centre of the bow and the drill shaft passed through the hole.

In the pump drill, alternating rotary motion of the drill is produced by up and down motion of the right hand, the left hand being used as before to hold a palm piece supporting the upper end of the drilling shaft. No bow is required, the cord passing through the axis of the drill spindle and having its two ends attached to the cross bar as shown in the illustration. As the cross bar is moved up and down the cord is wrapped round the drill spindle and the motion is maintained by the flywheel effect introduced by the mass of the stones in the coconut shell shown in the illustration. The operation of this form of drill takes a little practice but after a while the necessary skill is soon acquired and it will be found that this form of drill is more suitable for drilling larger holes while the bow drill is suitable for smaller holes. The spindle of the drill needs to be at least 16 in long between the top of the coconut shell and the palm piece so as to allow sufficient of the spindle for the cord to be wrapped round. The total length of the spindle (about 1 in in diameter) will then be rather more than 2 ft.

The origins of the pump drill are also lost in antiquity though it is generally believed to have been developed as a modification of the bow drill for special purposes such as drilling stone or porcelain. For this purpose it has been used up to the present century by itinerant craftsmen who used to repair broken chinaware with wire rivets passed through the holes in the china made with this device.

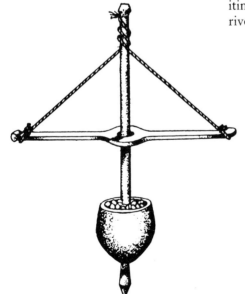

Pump drill from Nias, Indonesia, with a stone-filled coconut as flywheel

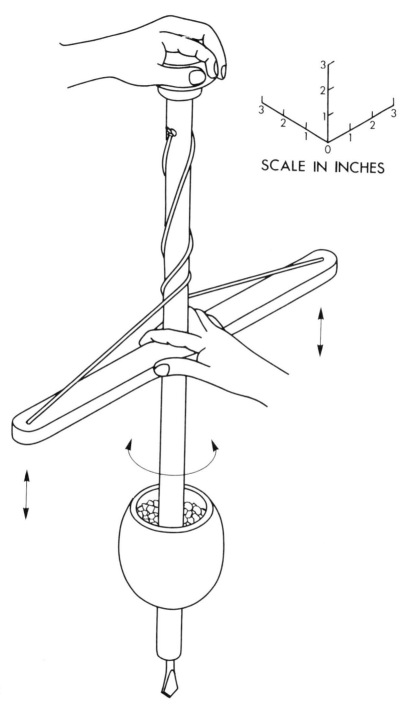

SCALE IN INCHES

Fig. 2/2   Pump drill

Bow Lathe

The bow lathe illustrated, Fig. 2/3, is, in principle, very similar to the bow drill, the major difference being that the workpiece is now rotating so that it can be cut with a stationary cutting tool supported on the horizontal bar which in turn is fixed parallel to the rotating workpiece. The workpiece is held between two horizontal round pegs which are mounted in the two vertical supports. The whole of the lathe can be made of wood as in the illustration, without any screws, nails or glueing, the necessary rigidity being achieved by wedges. The work is rotated alternately towards and away from the operator by moving the bow backwards and forwards.

The only tools required to make this lathe are a drill for drilling the holes, and a knife for tapering the wedges, and for tapering round dowelling that is used for making the centres between which the work is mounted. These centres are both known as *dead-centres* and can be held firmly in position by wedges and also by tying strong string or cord to them and to the supporting posts. The two dead-centres are tapered only at one end, the main portion being parallel so that they can slide in the vertical posts where they are wedged to the position required by tapered wedges of circular section which can be seen at the front of the picture. When these have been tapped home they locate the dead-centres in the position required to hold the workpiece easily.

Bow lathes of this type were used for hundreds of years for turning and particularly for doing fine work. They are unsuitable for heavy work because one hand must be used for the bow to rotate the work while the other holds the tool.

It is not known with any certainty when the lathe first came into use, though the remains of turned wooden vessels and amber beads were found in Asia Minor in graves of the seventh century B.C.

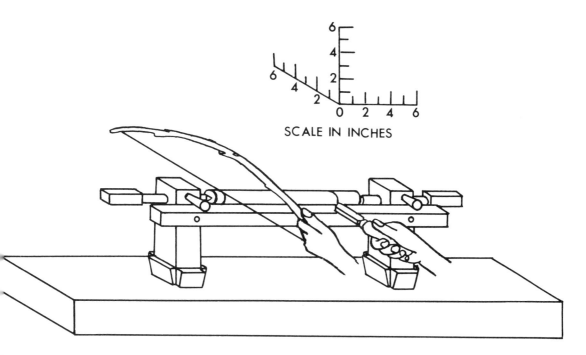

SCALE IN INCHES

Fig. 2/3   Bow lathe

Arab using bow lathe. Khan el Khalili Bazaar, Cairo, 1961

Pole and Tread Lathe

In this lathe, Fig. 2/4, which made its appearance in the Middle Ages, the work is rotated towards and away from the operator by using one foot on the treadle, leaving the operator with both hands free to hold the cutting tool.

The construction of the bed of the lathe, the vertical supports the horizontal tool rest and the two centres holding the work, are precisely the same as for the bow lathe but while the bow lathe can stand on a table, the pole and tread lathe requires its own framework since one end of the cord must pass down through the lathe bed to the treadle, while the other end of the cord is attached to one end of a green pole or sapling which is fixed roughly horizontal in the illustration, somewhat above the level of the head of the operator.

The framework on which the lathe bed is mounted in the illustration is built up of lengths of wood (broomsticks would do) fixed at each end with round wedges of dowelling so that the whole framework can be dismantled into small pieces for travelling. Alternately, it could be fixed to a more substantial framework provided that there was room for the treadle underneath. The size of the lathe can conveniently be made the same size as the bow lathe and the bed should stand about 3 ft from the ground.

The use of the green twig or sapling in which energy is temporarily stored as in a spring, to provide the return stroke, introduces new element into machine construction.

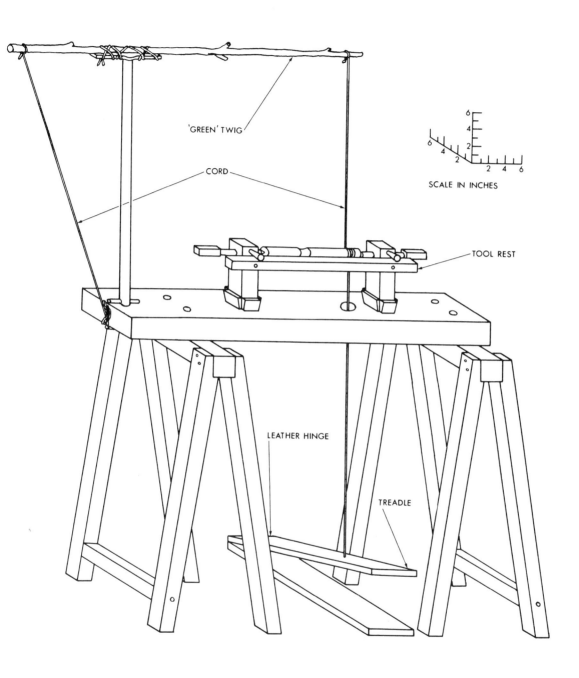

'GREEN' TWIG

CORD

SCALE IN INCHES

TOOL REST

LEATHER HINGE

TREADLE

ig. 2/4   Pole and tread lathe

The Great Wheel

The first lathe to be made with continuous rotary motion in the same direction and powered by men or animals was that driven by what was known in the Middle Ages as the Great Wheel. The workpiece was rotated between centres or between two bearings or overhung as in the figure, and driven by a crossed belt from the great wheel which was itself turned by cranks attached to either end of the great wheel shaft so that two strong men could turn it when heavy work such as metal turning was undertaken.

The illustration, Fig. 2/5, shows a great wheel 36 in in diameter mounted on a framework with its centre 42 in above the ground. An extension to the framework supporting the wheel supports a small lathe, which consists of a $\frac{1}{2}$ in steel shaft, 9 in long, mounted in two brass bushes 7 in apart, supported in a framework of hard-wood with a driving pulley half-way between the bearings. The Great Wheel itself needs to be supported on a substantial shaft preferably of metal say about $\frac{3}{4}$ in to 1 in in diameter, squared at either end to take the two handles. The work is fixed to a face plate or flange, attached to one end of the $\frac{1}{2}$ in diameter steel shaft and overhanging the two bearings so that turning can be done either on the circumference of the work or right across the face of the work parallel to the face-plate.

George Stephenson constructed the parts of his first steam locomotive in 1813 using a centre lathe driven by a great wheel turned by two strong men who found the work so arduous that they had to rest after every five minutes of working.

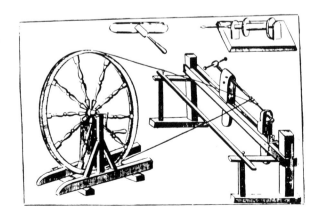

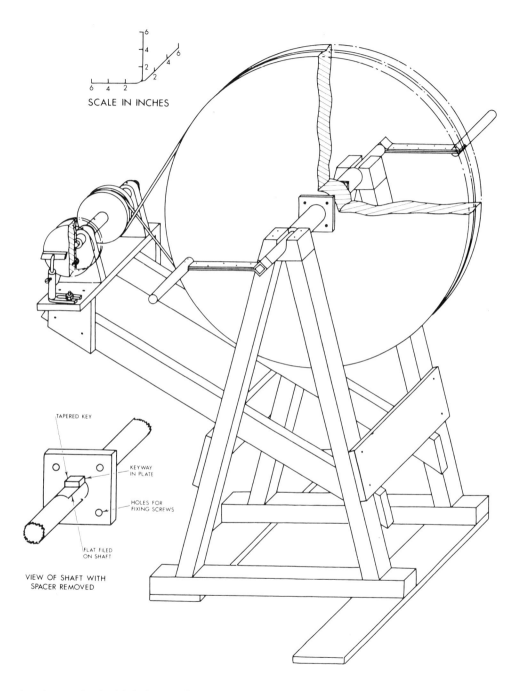

SCALE IN INCHES

TAPERED KEY

KEYWAY
IN PLATE

HOLES FOR
FIXING SCREWS

FLAT FILED
ON SHAFT

VIEW OF SHAFT WITH
SPACER REMOVED

Fig. 2/5   Great wheel with lathe attachment

Leonardo's Lathe

Leonardo da Vinci included in his notebooks a sketch of a treadle lathe with a flywheel, the lathe having one fixed centre and one running centre (Fig. 2/6). At this time, A.D. 1500, this was the first occasion that a lathe had been described that could be worked by a single operator having both hands free to use his tools and with the work rotating continuously in the same direction as in the lathe driven by the great wheel.

This type of lathe includes two machine elements that are essential parts of the design, namely, the flywheel and the crank, Fig. 2/6a. Both had been used previously in other machines but the combination as parts of a lathe was first recorded in Leonardo's notebook and this type of lathe has been used up to the present day as a foot operated lathe.

It is not easy to construct such a lathe full size without elaborate workshop facilities but a small working model about 6 in high and 12 in long could be made in a simple workshop provided that a metal flywheel about 8 in in diameter and steel crankshaft with a crank throw of about 1 in can be obtained. Details of such a model are shown in Fig. 2/6; most of the parts are of wood. The three bearings on the left of the running centre (one hidden) have their equivalents in a modern lathe in what is now called the *head-stock* of the lathe and the fixed or dead-centre with its screw attachment is to be found in the *poppet head* of the modern lathe, in which the poppet head can slide along the bed of the lathe. The workpiece has a pin attached to it through which it is driven by what is called a *carrier*. The carrier is a cranked pin fixed to the main spindle of the lathe. Leonardo's lathe has nothing equivalent to the bed of a modern lathe, in which the cutting tool can be made to slide parallel to the work with great accuracy.

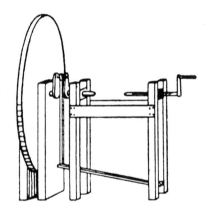

Leonardo's treadle lathe

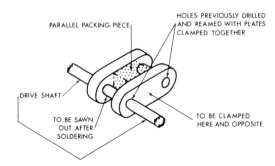

PARALLEL PACKING PIECE

HOLES PREVIOUSLY DRILLED
AND REAMED WITH PLATES
CLAMPED TOGETHER

DRIVE SHAFT

TO BE SAWN
OUT AFTER
SOLDERING

TO BE CLAMPED
HERE AND OPPOSITE

Fig. 2/6a Assembly of crank—
Leonardo da Vinci's treadle lathe

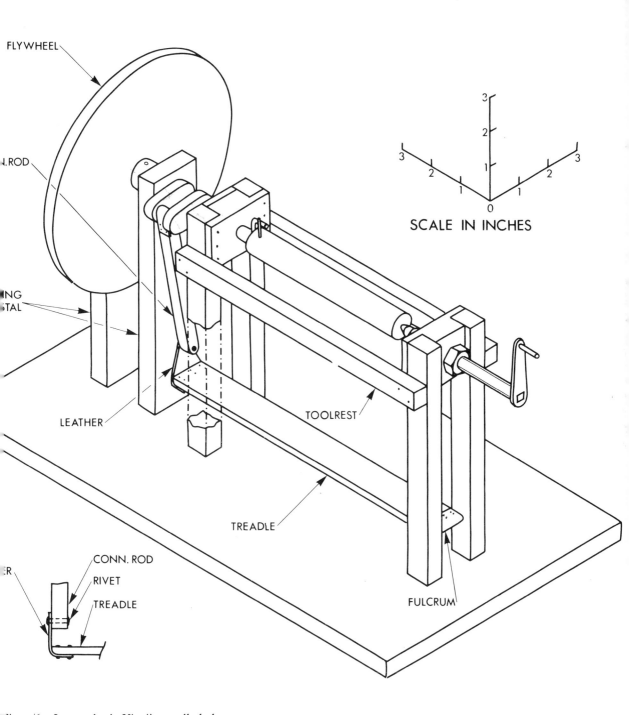

FLYWHEEL

N.ROD

NG
TAL

LEATHER

TOOLREST

TREADLE

CONN. ROD

R

RIVET

TREADLE

FULCRUM

SCALE IN INCHES

Fig. 2/6   Leonardo da Vinci's treadle lathe

23

Hero's Screw Cutter

Male screw threads were made in Greek times as part of screw presses for pressing grapes and olives and for other purposes, and the nuts associated with these screws consisted of a hollow block of wood into the side of which a number of pins were driven to catch in the grooves between the screw threads. These had the defect that they damaged the screw thread when great pressure was used and some means was required for making a female screw thread that would fit accurately on a male screw thread. Such a female screw thread is found in nuts that are used with bolts today.

The first to devise a method for making a female screw thread from a male screw thread was Hero of Alexandria who described it in one of his writings about A.D. 100. The device is shown in Fig 2/7 from which it will be clear that an internal thread can be cut with the single-point tool that has been inserted into the right-hand end of the screw spindle. As the master screw is turned by hand from the left-hand end, it moves the single-point tool, thus forming, on the inside diameter of the work-piece, an internal helix that exactly corresponds to the external helix of the master screw. This is brought about by the three pins shown at the middle of the diagram. These pins have ends shaped to engage with the thread of the screw so that as the latter is turned around it moves forward with the same pitch as the pitch of the screw.

The device shown in the illustration is a wooden block 3 in × 3 in × 4 in and the nut is formed in a piece of transparent plastic such as perspex, this being $2\frac{1}{2}$ in square by $\frac{1}{2}$ in thick. The hole in the block of wood is $1\frac{1}{2}$ in diameter and the screw has four threads per inch. To make a nut to fit on this screw it is necessary to wind the cutting tool through the nut about fifty times, the point of the tool being tapped forward to make a deeper cut each time.

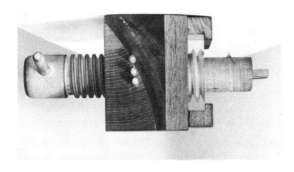

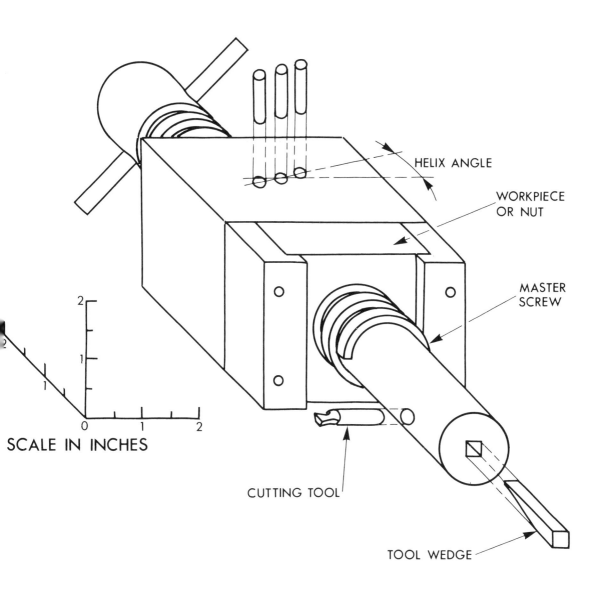

HELIX ANGLE

WORKPIECE
OR NUT

MASTER
SCREW

SCALE IN INCHES

CUTTING TOOL

TOOL WEDGE

Fig. 2/7   Hero's screw cutter

25

Screw Generating Device

One of the questions frequently asked of the engineering apprentice is "How would you generate a screw thread on a round piece of bar if you had no taps, or dies, or 'chasers', or a lathe having a lead screw?" These methods, which are used for making screw threads in the workshop, are all ways of copying an existing screw thread. Likewise Hero's screw-cutting device mentioned above is a method of copying a male thread in order to make a female thread.

At least two ways of making a screw thread without copying are believed to have been used in very ancient times, one was to wrap around the bar on which the screw was to be formed, a parallel strip of leather or gut, the pitch at which the wrapping was done being that of the screw to be produced. Then, with a fine saw and chisel a screw could be formed by cutting away material between the strip of leather or gut. This method produced a square thread on the bar but it was not very accurate. Another method was to wrap round the plain bar a triangular sheet of flexible material, metal or leather, which had been cut to form a triangle with the helix angle of the thread desired.

Neither of these methods is as elegant as the screw generating device that came into use about two hundred years ago in England and was certainly used by the famous English toolmaker Henry Maudslay, to make the lead screws for his all-metal screw-cutting lathe. The screw-generating device shown in the picture, Fig. 2/8, is made mainly of wood and the picture shows a plan and elevation of the device drawn to the scale shown. The workpiece is a broom-handle of $1\frac{1}{4}$ in in diameter and it will be seen from the picture that the angle of the thread is determined by the tilt of the "pitch blade" at the left-hand side. The thread is finally cut by the tool at the right-hand side, the workpiece being rotated by hand gripping each end of the broom-handle and turning it around. The pitch blade is made of steel and is inserted into a piece of brass or copper tubing to which it has been soldered. This tube is locked in a wooden grip having metal faces with two steel locking bolts passing through the top of the grip as shown on the drawing. The grip holding the pitch blade is located by a small metal angle so that it is constrained to move at right-angles to the workpiece when the pitch blade screw is turned. Likewise, the cutting tool is mounted on a wooden block with a metal face and there are two steel strips across the top of the tool and two metal angle pieces to constrain the tool to move at right-angles to the workpiece when the tool feed is operated. The block holding the cutting tool is secured to the

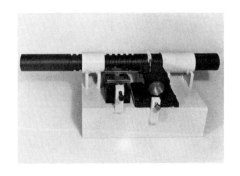

base by the four screws which hold the cutting tool. This device needs to be clamped to a table while the workpiece is being rotated by hand.

ELEVATION WITH WORKPIECE REMOVED

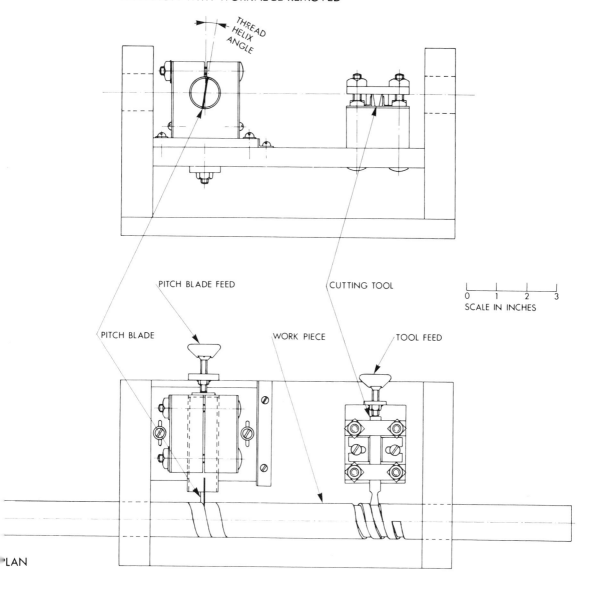

Fig. 2/8   Screw generator

The Oliver

One of the ancient machine tools that is little known is a treadle-operated tilt hammer known as the Oliver. Used by blacksmiths in the Middle Ages it enabled a single blacksmith to operate a heavy sledge hammer with his foot, the hammer being lifted by a green sapling similar to that used in the pole and tread lathe. If made to the full scale it would occupy too much space but the principle can be illustrated just as well in a small model made mainly of wood to the scale shown on the diagram, Fig. 2/9. The metal parts consist of the anvil itself, the hammer head, a wire yoke, two fine chains, and the metal strap at the right-hand end of the green sapling. The apparatus needs to be adjusted so that the hammer will just strike the anvil when the hammer shaft is slightly below the horizontal.

Normally, when used for forging, the thickness of the metal—such as a horseshoe or other article being forged will cause the blow to be delivered while the hammer shaft is horizontal. The movable prop allows for tensioning of the green twig or sapling which needs to be replaced when it has lost its spring.

The Oliver

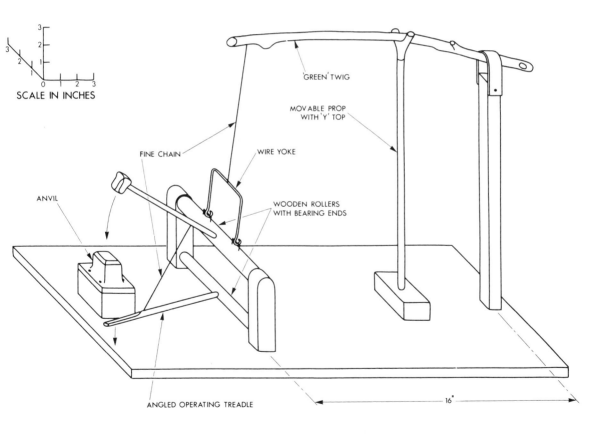

SCALE IN INCHES

'GREEN' TWIG

MOVABLE PROP
WITH 'Y' TOP

FINE CHAIN

WIRE YOKE

ANVIL

WOODEN ROLLERS
WITH BEARING ENDS

16"

ANGLED OPERATING TREADLE

Fig. 2/9   The Oliver—treadle hammer

Chapter III   Lifting Devices

Lever and Slip Knot

One of the most important machine elements in lifting devices is the lever. This was the essential part of the method used traditionally by Chinese builders for raising heavy weights. An assembly of rods and ropes put together in the manner shown in the sketch can be used to illustrate the method and at the same time to impress upon the user the mechanical advantage to be gained by using a lever with unequal arms. The lever is suspended from a rope attached about a quarter of the distance from its left-hand end, the lifting rope being attached as near to the left-hand end as possible. The rope to which the builder applies his strength—the hauling rope—is attached to the right-hand end of the lever, thus giving him a mechanical advantage of 3 : 1 in the sketch. Another rope—the steady rope—is attached to the heavy weight being lifted to hold it in position while a fresh bite is taken with the lifting rope, to raise the weight still further. The steady rope and the lifting rope are joined together by a slip knot—the rolling hitch—which has to be pulled down by hand each time a fresh bite is taken with the lifting rope.

All that is required to make up this assembly is a framework with three horizontal bars, a heavy weight, a lever say 18 in long, and a quantity of rope sufficiently strong for the weight that is to be lifted. The framework shown, Fig. 3/1, was made up of broom-shanks and wooden corner pieces drilled and pinned.

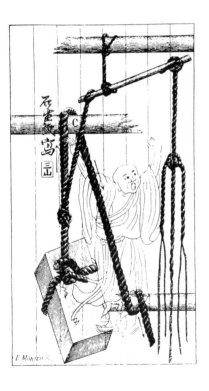

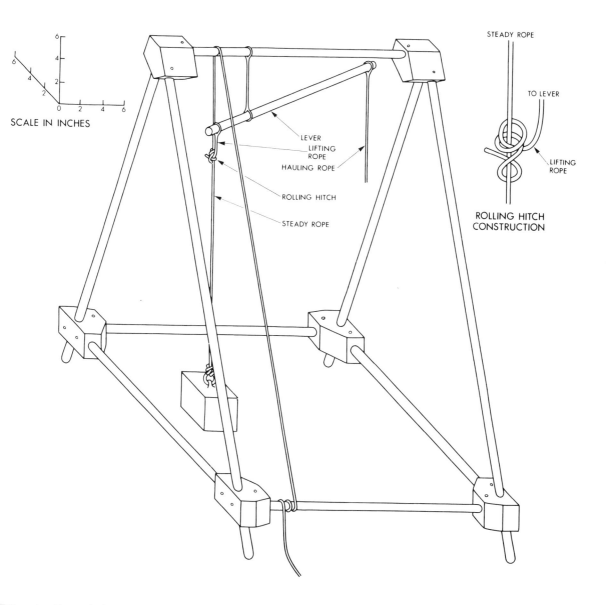

SCALE IN INCHES

STEADY ROPE

TO LEVER

LEVER

LIFTING ROPE

LIFTING ROPE

HAULING ROPE

ROLLING HITCH

STEADY ROPE

ROLLING HITCH
CONSTRUCTION

Fig. 3/1   Lever hoist

The Simple Pulley

The origin of the simple pulley—one of the most important mechanical inventions—is lost in antiquity. An early picture found in Sumeria is dated about 800 B.C. In making the model the pulley wheel itself needs to be approximately round, and grooved to take a lifting rope. It need not necessarily be turned, it can be whittled with a knife. All the parts shown can be made of wood. The fixed axle on which the pulley rotates should be a neat fit in the hole in the centre of the pulley. This axle passes through the centre of the two side members of the frame and is located by two wooden pegs passing through the axle just outside the frame. The frame itself has cross members in addition to the two side members and all these are fastened together by wooden pegs—dowels—as indicated. The whole assembly is suspended by a rope passing through the centre of the top member so that it hangs vertically. The weight to be lifted is attached to one end of the rope which passes round the pulley and the operator pulls down on the other end of the rope to lift the weight which thereupon rises.

The principal use of this application of the pulley in early times and even today, is in building work where one wishes to lift a fairly heavy weight such as a bucket containing sand, from the ground up to the top of the building. One of the limitations of this simple device, Fig. 3/2, is that there is no *mechanical advantage* (the operator must exert the same force as is required to lift the weight) and if the operator lets go of the rope at any time the weight being lifted will fall with increasing velocity to the ground.

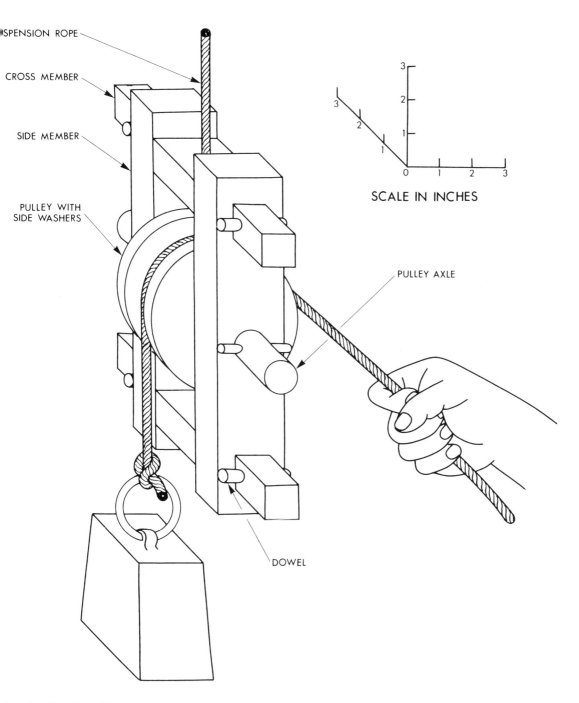

SPENSION ROPE

CROSS MEMBER

SIDE MEMBER

PULLEY WITH
SIDE WASHERS

PULLEY AXLE

DOWEL

3
3
2
2
1
1
0   1   2   3

SCALE IN INCHES

ig. 3/2   Simple pulley

Simple Pulley with Ratchet and Pawl

A ratchet and pawl constitutes another important element in many machines. It is used in modern mechanical clocks and wheels. The Romans had previously used such a device in their large catapults, or onagers, for throwing heavy stone balls.

By fixing a ratchet and pawl to the pulley and fastening the pulley to its axle, to which the ratchet is attached, the weight lifted by the pulley can be held automatically in the position to which it has been lifted, i.e. the motion cannot be reversed without releasing the pawl.

The illustration, Fig. 3/3, shows a model pulley with ratchet and pawl that can easily be made by the enthusiastic amateur. The ratchet plate is of steel with sixteen teeth and the pulley is held in contact with these teeth at all times by the spiral tension spring. The ratchet wheel can be cut out by hand, using a small fine hack saw and finishing off with a file. Otherwise most of the work involved in making up this pulley is in drilling the holes. To obtain a really firm fixing of the pulley to the shaft—an essential feature of this model—the method already described for the great wheel may be used; for fixing the ratchet wheel, the end of the shaft may be squared with a file.

Fig. 3/3   Pulley with ratchet and pawl

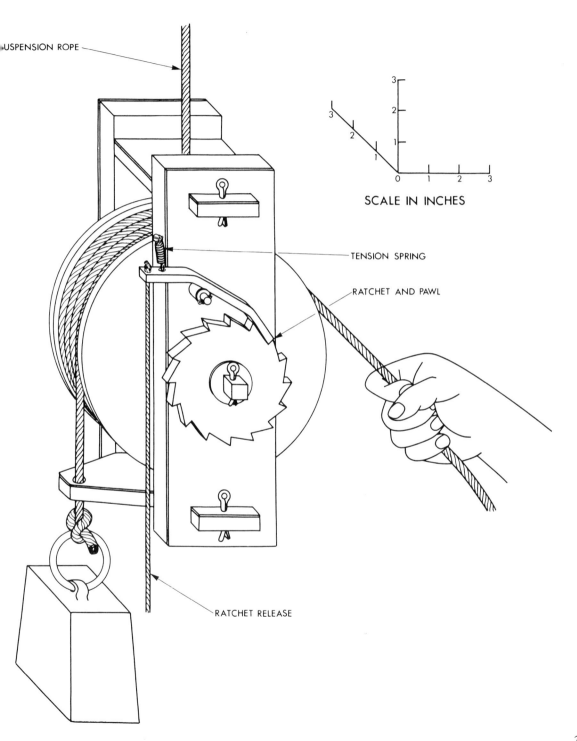

USPENSION ROPE

SCALE IN INCHES

TENSION SPRING

RATCHET AND PAWL

RATCHET RELEASE

Multiple Pulleys

The use of two or more pulleys to lift a heavy weight is almost as old as the use of a single pulley and the origins of both are obscure. Multiple pulleys of various kinds were described by many writers in Greek and Roman times. In the compound pulley a single rope is passed successively round two pulleys as in Fig. 3/4; in the triple pulley the rope is passed successively round three pulleys. Several authors have stated that Archimedes invented both the triple and compound pulley which he used in his remarkable demonstration of dragging single-handed a fully laden ship across dry land.

The feature of multiple pulleys that is so valuable is that the force required to lift a given weight is almost inversely proportional to the number of pulleys used. (The effect of friction only becomes significant when a large number of pulleys are coupled together.

The reduction in the force required to lift a weight that results from using multiple pulleys is one example of mechanical advantage and can be demonstrated most effectively by coupling together the two previous models in the manner shown in Fig. 3/4.

Fig. 3/4 Compound pulley

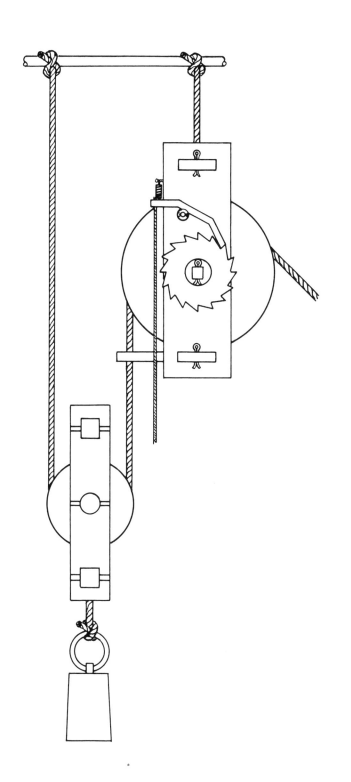

The Chinese Windlass

The Chinese or differential windlass is a most impressive example of mechanical advantage since it enables the operator, by exerting quite a small force, to lift a very large weight. The illustration, Fig. 3/5, shows a drum round which the lifting rope is wound, the drum having two different diameters, being slightly larger (e.g. 3/32 inches) at the left-hand end, than it is at the right-hand end. The weight being lifted is 28 lb which can be lifted by the application of only 10 oz at the operating handle. The frame is made of wood, the axle of the differential pulley simply resting in grooves at the top of each of the vertical supports. The differential pulley itself could be made of either wood or metal.

The origins of the Chinese Windlass are obscure. Its modern equivalent is the Weston Differential Pulley in which an endless chain is used in place of rope and the pulleys are deeply grooved with lugs to engage the links of the chain.

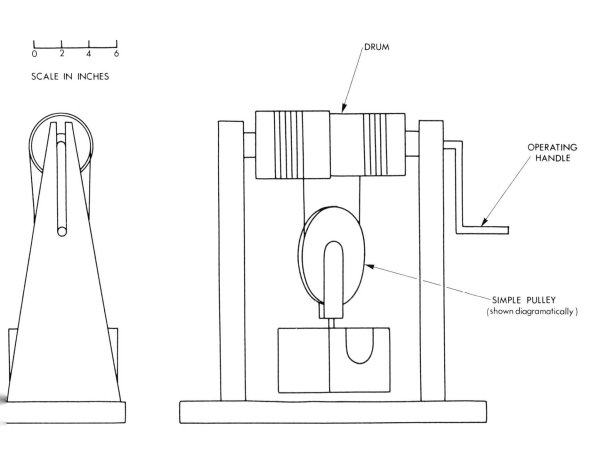

SCALE IN INCHES

DRUM

OPERATING
HANDLE

SIMPLE PULLEY
(shown diagramatically)

Fig. 3/5   Chinese windlass (differential pulley)

The Arabian Grappling Device

A simple mechanism for lifting objects from the ground or from a river bed was described in some Arabic literature about A.D. 900. It is still used in modern mechanical grabs.

The model illustrated, Fig. 3/6, is made of two halves of a piece of copper tubing, the upper edges of the tubing are hinged together and the bottom edges have been serrated so as to catch more easily on objects that are being lifted. The construction and method of operation can be seen in the diagram.

When operating the grab, it is convenient to place two fingers of the left hand under the square frame—if these are lifted then the grab will open—and at the same time to insert the right forefinger in the ring at the top of the picture—if this is lifted, the grab will close.

To demonstrate the action the grab should be lowered in the open position on top of the object to be lifted—say a string of beads; the grab is then closed by lifting the circular ring with the right forefinger: this will first close the grab and then lift the string of beads.

By working the grab using two hands together, skill in its use is quickly acquired.

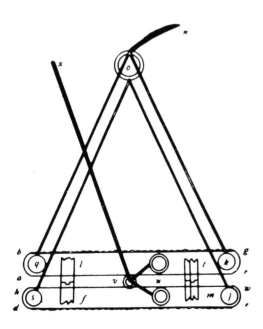

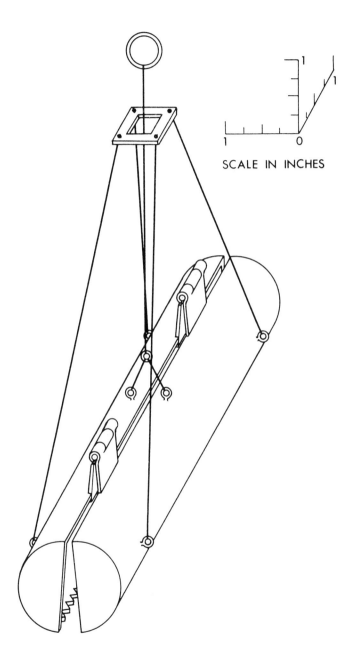

SCALE IN INCHES

1

1

1   0

Fig. 3/6   Arabian grappling device

Shadouf

The swape or shadouf, still used in Egypt for irrigation purposes is extremely old and it is especially interesting to mechanical engineers as a mechanism for it embodies the principle of the lever, mechanical advantage and the use of a downward pull in order to lift water upwards. Above all, it includes a most elegant arrangement for suspending the fulcrum pin which allows the bucket to be moved from side to side as well as up and down. It also avoids the necessity for lubrication that would be so difficult in desert conditions and would also constrain the motion of the lever and prevent the sideways movement which is such an advantage.

The model, Fig. 3/7, has in the main been built of a green branch, the fulcrum pin being nearest to the left-hand end where a heavy bob is formed round the end of the twig from wet clay and straw, though in the model the addition of some cement is an advantage. The bucket is made of leather and is conical in shape with a stone or lead weight at the bottom so that it always sinks below the surface of the water into which it is dipped. The operator works by pulling downwards on the cord joining the bucket to the right-hand end of the twig. The cord used is strong machine thread, similar thread or twine can be used to suspend the fulcrum pin from the fixed cross-bar on which it is supported.

For demonstration, two small tanks or bowls are required to contain the water. The leather bucket is dipped down into the first and when the bucket has been filled and lifted by the counter-weight, the contents are tipped into a runnel down which the water runs into the other tank. The model is mounted on four legs to support it well above the table.

Although this device is so old that its origins are unknown, it is still in use in some Eastern countries.

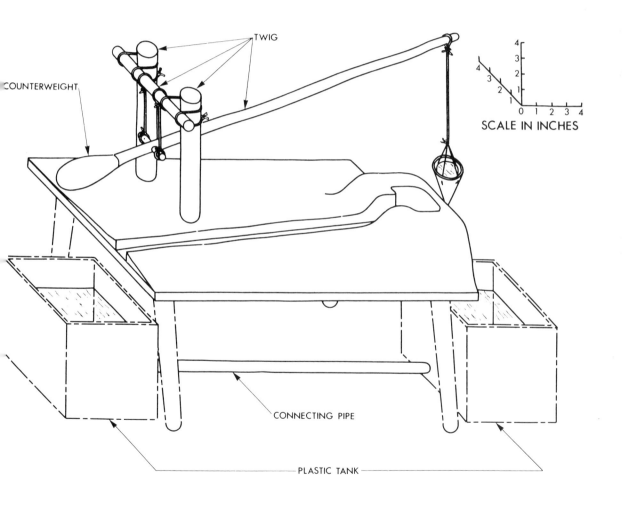

TWIG

COUNTERWEIGHT

4
3
2
1
4
3
2
1
0 1 2 3 4
SCALE IN INCHES

CONNECTING PIPE

PLASTIC TANK

Fig. 3/7   Shadouf

The Chinese Spoon-tilt Hammer

For heavy hammering, forging metal, fulling cloth and other purposes where a heavy hammer was required, it was traditional in China to use the Chinese spoon-tilt hammer. It consisted of a long wooden lever hinged near its centre and with one end hollowed out to the shape of a spoon. A torrent of water came down a chute into the spoon and at the other end of the lever the hammer head was attached. The force of the water pushed the spoon down lifting the hammer head which then fell when the spoon had moved out of the path of the water and emptied itself. The hammer end of the lever being thus heavier, the spoon rose again and was refilled with water automatically. Similar devices were used in Japan.

A small version of this device can be made and operated very simply by mounting an ordinary tablespoon on the end of a lever with a hammer head at its other end, as shown in the picture, Fig 3/8. The spoon and its mounting can then be placed inside a small plastic baby's bath which can be purchased quite cheaply, and another plastic bowl slightly smaller can be mounted above the spoon with a small $\frac{1}{4}$ in pipe and cock coming from it. The flow of water from the upper bowl will then operate the spoon until the upper tank is empty. The spoon will empty itself into the bath so that the same lot of water can be used again if it is pumped or baled from the lower tank back into the other one.

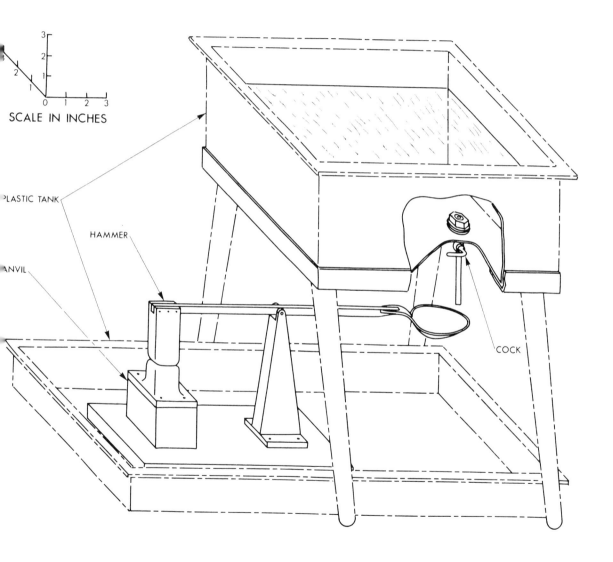

SCALE IN INCHES

PLASTIC TANK

HAMMER

ANVIL

COCK

Fig. 3/8   Spoon-tilt hammer

45

The Cornish Man Engine

The Cornish Man Engine was a machine used during the last century and in the early part of this century, in the mines in Cornwall, for taking miners down the pit at the beginning of a shift and bringing them up at the end of a shift instead of requiring them to walk up and down ladders which was a time wasting alternative. It was also used for bringing material up out of the pit, a process which involved miners standing one on each step on the way down, to move sacks of the material on and off the moving platforms as they came to rest opposite a stationary platform at each end of the stroke of the machine.

The man engine consisted of a strong square wooden post extending right down the pit shaft and having platforms fixed at one side at intervals of seven or eight feet all the way down the pit. Fixed platforms were also attached to the walls of the pit at similar intervals down the pit shaft. The long square post was moved up and down with a stroke of seven or eight feet according to the distance between the platforms and as it momentarily came to rest at each end of its stroke, men or material were moved from the central moving platforms to the fixed ones on the wall of the shaft. The rod was oscillated up and down by a steam engine through gearing and bell cranks.

For a model, the engine can be dispensed with and the apparatus turned by hand using a small crank attached to the gear-wheel shown in the sketch, Fig. 3/9. The distance between the platforms was chosen to suit the size of the toy men that can be obtained from a toy shop. Except for the links, the bell crank and the gears which are of metal, the remainder of the model is made of wood.

Fig. 3/9   Cornish Man Engine

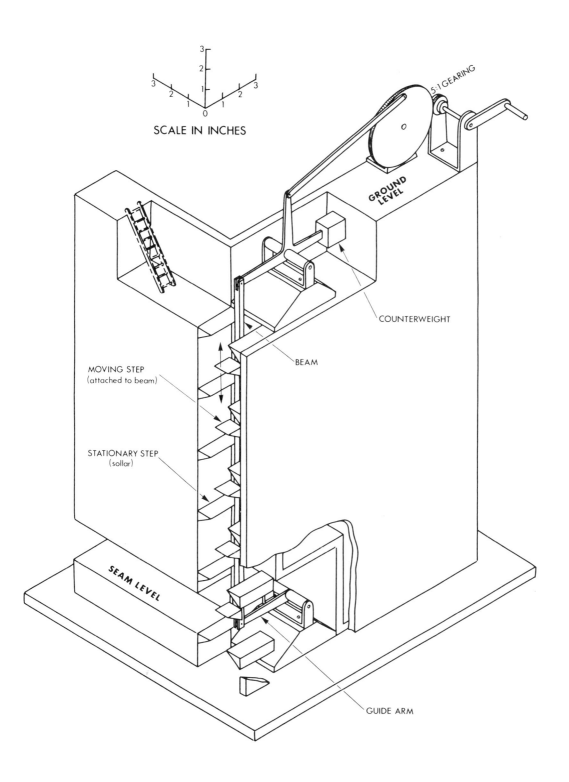

3
2
1
3   1   1   2   3
2   0   1
1

SCALE IN INCHES

5:1 GEARING

GROUND LEVEL

COUNTERWEIGHT

BEAM

MOVING STEP
(attached to beam)

STATIONARY STEP
(sollar)

SEAM LEVEL

GUIDE ARM

47

Chapter IV   Mechanisms

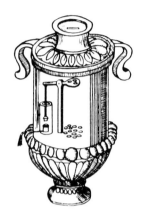

Coin-in-the-slot Machine

A simple mechanism that can easily be made is seen in the working parts of the coin-in-the-slot machine, as used in temples in ancient Greece to encourage the faithful to pay their tribute for a libation of holy water. In its early form it consisted of a stone vessel, cylindrical in shape, having a base and a lid, in the centre of which was a slot for inserting the coin. The libation of holy water issued from a spout on the side of the stone vessel near the bottom.

For simplicity one can use a canister of transparent plastic material such as polystyrene, obtainable cheaply at multiple stores. The construction can be seen from the illustration, Fig. 4/1, and the outside view, Fig. 4/1a, of a model in which a standard canister was used and modified as shown. In this case the adhesive used throughout was Araldite—an epoxy resin. When in operation, the model is partly filled with water and when a coin is inserted into the slot it falls down a chute into the water striking one end of the beam and thus momentarily lifting the other end which serves as a stopper to close the outlet. Thus a small amount of water issues for a short time through the outlet and then when the coin falls into the base of the container the valve recloses because that end is heavier than the other end of the beam. The beam and its central support and the stopper closing the hole are all made of brass, the outlet pipe is copper, but the remainder of the model is constructed of plastic.

When using this device for demonstrations, it is sometimes useful to have a tightly fitting cover over the whole of the outside of the apparatus with a slot in the top, the cover being made of cartridge paper or cardboard. It is revealing to invite those who put their coins into the slot to try and guess what kind of mechanism can deliver the same quantity of water from the outlet every time a coin is dropped in. The cover can later be removed to demonstrate the operation of the model.

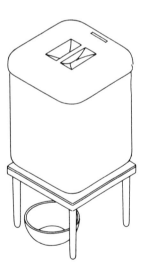

Fig. 4/1a External view—
coin-in-the-slot machine

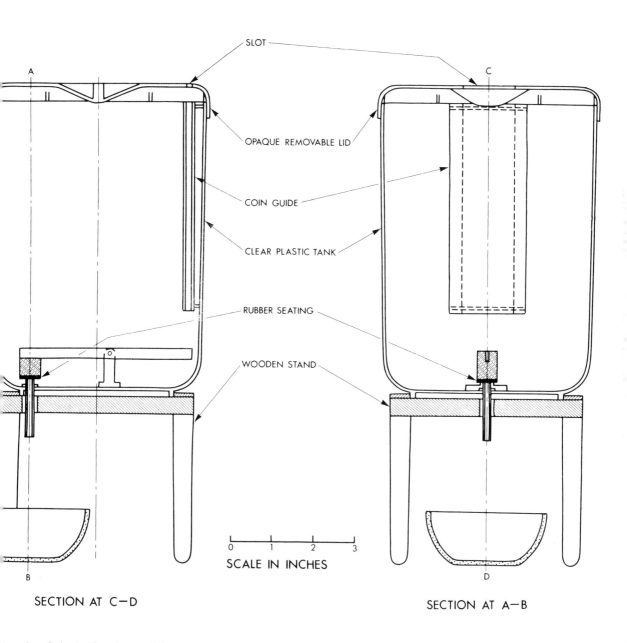

SLOT

OPAQUE REMOVABLE LID

COIN GUIDE

CLEAR PLASTIC TANK

RUBBER SEATING

WOODEN STAND

SCALE IN INCHES

0   1   2   3

SECTION AT C—D

SECTION AT A—B

ᴵg. 4/ɪ   Coin-in-the-slot machine

49

The Greek Puppet Theatre Mechanism

An interesting device described by Hero of Alexandria in A.D. 100 was used by the Greeks for the automatic operation of the carriage of a puppet theatre. It consisted as shown in the illustration, Fig. 4/2, of a wooden carriage mounted on three wheels which were caused to move by the falling of a heavy weight inside a hopper of square cross-section. The rate of fall of this weight was controlled by the escape of rape-seed from inside the hopper through a small orifice at the base. To the upper face of the weight, which was also square in cross-section, a cord was attached which passed round two pulleys to the axle of the two front wheels, thus driving the carriage backwards or forward according to which way round the axle the cord was wound. A feature of this apparatus was that with a single charge of rape-seed the carriage could be caused to move first forward and then backwards by winding the cord partly one way round the axle, then round a pin through the axle shaft and then the reverse way round the axle.

In the model illustrated, Fig. 4/2, the hopper is made of tin plate or hardboard as is the slide or control valve at the base of the hopper which closes the orifice. The rape-seed as it issues there from falls into a rectangular box—(a biscuit-tin suffices).

When giving demonstrations of these models to schoolboys, the author has found this to be one of the most popular of those described in this book. The model illustrated has a rectangular carriage with three wheels and is driven by the two front wheels.

It is important that the weight resting on top of the bed of rape seed should be sufficiently heavy. The model has a heavy metal weight resting on top of the wooden piston. The edges of the weight are rounded, so as to cause as little friction as possible as it falls down through the cylinder. To operate the model the control valve slide is first closed and the piston and weight lifted out, turning the pulley bracket in its bearings so that the top of the hopper is open to receive the rape-seed which can be poured in directly from the biscuit-tin if the latter is moved backwards and then lifted into position suitable for pouring the seed into the hopper. The piston and weight must then be placed back in the cylinder taking care that the piston is exactly horizontal. The cord can then be tightened by turning the front wheels, when the carriage is ready to start as soon as the control valve is opened. Great care must be taken to ensure a good fit between the hopper and its piston. This apparatus is one of the first examples known of the use of a heavy

weight falling under gravity in a controlled manner, the fall of
the weight being used to perform useful work.

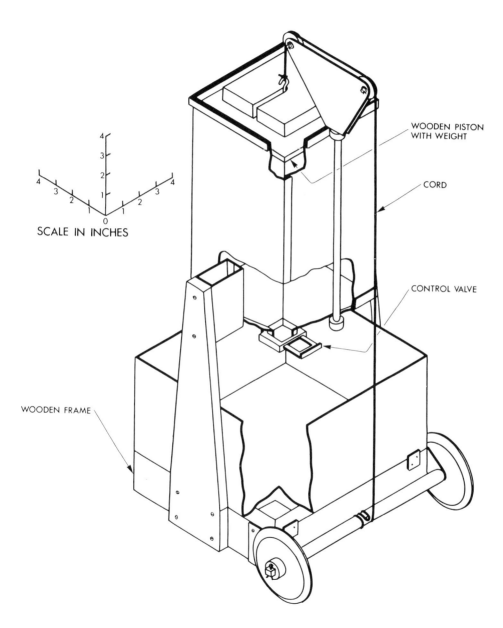

SCALE IN INCHES

WOODEN PISTON
WITH WEIGHT

CORD

CONTROL VALVE

WOODEN FRAME

Fig. 4/2   Greek puppet theatre mechanism

The Chinese South-pointing Chariot

A mechanism of an entirely different kind is the model of the Chinese south-pointing chariot, as shown in the illustration, Fig 4/3. A full-scale machine of this kind was used in ceremonial processions in China between A.D. 120 and 250. It seems that its purpose must have been simply to cause awe and wonder in the onlookers since whichever way the chariot was turned the figure on the top always pointed in the same direction. This intriguing result was obtained by means of differential gearing, very similar to that used in the back-axle of the present-day motor vehicle Possibly pin gears were used in the originals, though this is no certain.

The diagrammatic sketch, Fig. 4/3, shows how the wheels would be coupled together if the drive were merely friction of the edge o one wheel on the edge of the next, but this arrangement would be unsatisfactory in practice. A working model can however conveniently be made using standard gears, and for the model with two road wheels $3\frac{1}{2}$ in in diameter and $3\frac{1}{2}$ in apart, two pairs of spu gears are required and four pairs of bevel gears all with the same numbers of teeth. The wheels are coupled up through the gearing as shown in the diagram and the figure on the top is supported on a triangular base which is in turn supported from the frame of the carriage. The triangular platform supporting the figure is made that particular shape so as to provide support for the gear-wheel connecting the operating end of the differential to one of the side wheels, the other side wheel is coupled to the lower end of the differential. The figure at the top is connected to the planetar axle of the differential as shown in the diagram.

This model is well worth making by anyone who has the mean of obtaining accurately cut gear-wheels. These are essential, and the amateur should not be encouraged to try and manufactur gear-wheels for himself since they will not have the necessar accuracy.

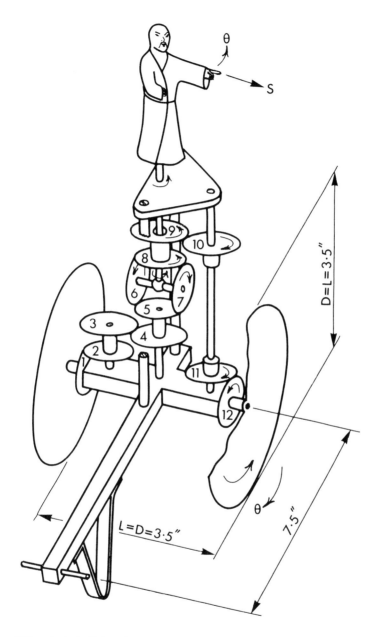

Wheels 1, 2; 5, 6, 7, 8; 11, 12:– Bevel gears, 1:1 ratio
Wheels 3, 4; 9, 10:– Spur gears, 1:1 ratio

Fig. 4/3   South-pointing chariot

Foliot and Verge Escapement

The most important machine element in mechanical clockwork is known as the *escapement*. This is the device which was used to operate all the early tower clocks by controlling the fall of the driving weight. It is not known who invented the earliest form of mechanical escapement. The foliot balance and verge, which first appeared in tower clocks about 1350, continued in use as the only mechanical escapement for tower clocks for nearly three centuries. A man who had learned to make and repair this apparatus was known as a *clockmaker* and such men were in great demand to make and supervise many other mechanical devices.

The essential elements of the foliot and verge escapement are shown in the diagram, Fig. 4/4, where it will be seen that the horizontal beam (or verge) with weights at either end, oscillates about the vertical axis being suspended from a piece of strong nylon thread which can be seen at the top-centre of the diagram. The working model stands 26 in from the table on a square base and the supports are long enough to allow the operating weight to fall a total height of 15 in. The time taken depends upon the size of the balance weights and their position on the verge. The further out these balance weights are placed the slower is the period of oscillation of the verge. An essential element of the escapement is the two pallets fixed to the vertical staff which engage alternately with the teeth at the top and bottom of the large toothed wheel at the centre of the diagram. This is a saucer-shaped wheel with contrate teeth in the edge of the saucer. There are thirty teeth in the model described and this can be manufactured by hand with a fine saw and a file. The spur gears between the spindle of the main toothed wheel and the spindle round which the cord is attached are inserted to provide for a longer operation of the escapement for a given fall of the weight. Without these gears which provide an eight to one reduction, the weight would fall far too quickly. All the parts of this model—both the moving parts and the structure—should be made of metal if reasonably accurate timing is to be obtained.

One of the earliest foliot and verge escapements was that in the tower clock in Dover Castle. The clock itself has been preserved in the Science Museum, South Kensington, London, where it can often be seen in operation.

From a technical point of view this model is the most important mechanism so far described and it is surely of great interest to the amateur to be able to make for himself a machine that will work automatically so long as the weight is falling.

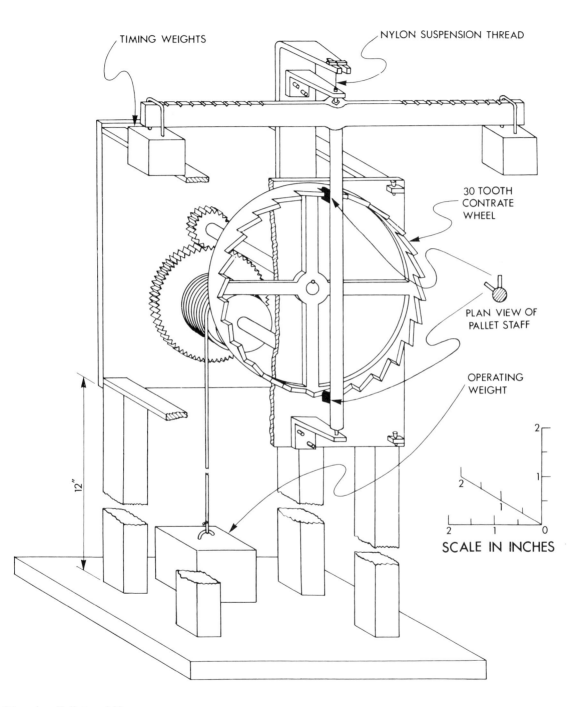

TIMING WEIGHTS

NYLON SUSPENSION THREAD

30 TOOTH
CONTRATE
WHEEL

PLAN VIEW OF
PALLET STAFF

OPERATING
WEIGHT

12"

2
1
2
1
1
0
2

SCALE IN INCHES

Fig. 4/4   Foliot and Verge escapement

The Wrapping Escapement

Somewhat easier to make than the foliot and verge, is the wrapping escapement, sometimes known as the flyball escapement, which is the essential feature of a type of clock invented in Germany about 1870, and still used on some clocks that are sold today. This escapement is not an accurate one but it is easier for the amateur to make than the conventional type of clockwork which requires highly accurate machining of the parts.

In this device the falling weight is restrained periodically by the wrapping and unwrapping of a thread round a fixed vertical wrapping post and static wrapping arm. One end of the thread is fixed to the end of a swinging radius arm which is rotated by the falling weight and to the other end of this thread a small weight is attached so that it flies out as it rotates. The model illustrated, Fig. 4/5, has two vertical posts (the wrapping posts), 180° apart and 3 in from the central tube to which the radius arm is attached. These two wrapping posts are fixed rigidly to the platform at their lower ends and are not quite high enough to reach the swinging arm which flies round over the top of them. Through the centre of the tube supporting the swinging arm there is a fixed post, to which the static wrapping arm is attached. The two ends of this arm extend beyond the posts and clear of them and have prongs bending downwards and also bent inwards so that as the flying ball meets the prongs it is forced to wrap the thread around the fixed post, first one way and then the other, and it automatically unwraps and releases itself so that the swinging arm can move another 180° before it is arrested by the ball wrapping the thread around the next post. Some experimental trials when the apparatus is first assembled will show the most suitable value for the angle between the posts and the static wrapping arm. As with all mechanical escapements operated by weights, the fall of the weight can be used for a longer period if multiple gears are used between the rotating member of the escapement and the drum round which the cord of the weight is wound. For this model hardboard and wood are suitable materials for the structure.

Fig. 4/5   Wrapping escapement

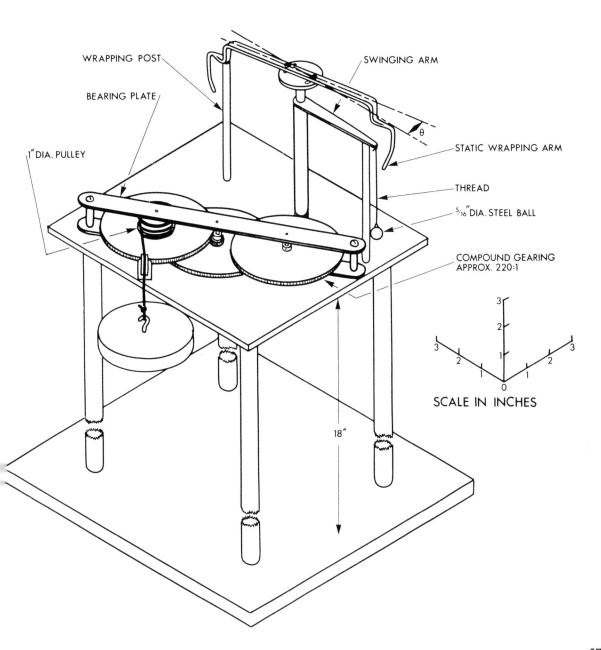

WRAPPING POST

BEARING PLATE

1" DIA. PULLEY

SWINGING ARM

θ

STATIC WRAPPING ARM

THREAD

$\frac{5}{16}$" DIA. STEEL BALL

COMPOUND GEARING
APPROX. 220:1

3
2
1
3
2
1
0
1
2
3

SCALE IN INCHES

18"

Chapter V   Machines for Pumping and Water Raising

Archimedean Snail

In ancient times a great deal of irrigation of dry land was done by raising water in the archimedean screw or archimedean snail.

Fig. 5/1 shows a simplified version of it that can be made very easily if a long length of flexible plastic tubing can be obtained. By wrapping the tubing around a wooden cylinder to form a spiral and mounting the axis of the cylinder in bearings held in a suitable framework of wood or metal, we have the essential parts of an unusual type of pump or water raising device.

The axis of the cylinder needs to be inclined about 25°–30° to the horizontal and the lower end of the coil of pipe must dip into water as the cylinder is rotated. Water will then be forced up through the coil by the rotation and emerge from the top end of the coil of pipe whence it can be allowed to fall back into the rectangular tank—not shown—in which the model should be mounted.

Rotation of the whole coil in this model is effected by turning the crank at the right-hand end, this crank being attached to the axis of the coil. It should be remembered that the crank in this form was probably not known at the time when the snail pump was in general use. In those days the operator—usually a slave—turned the drum by treading with his feet on steps attached to the spindle while holding with his hands on a cross-bar fixed to the ground.

In ancient times another version of the archimedean screw was used for raising water. Usually this consisted of a large spiral screw that was rotated inside a fixed wooden casing suitably inclined to the horizontal. Sometimes casing and screw were rotated together. In either case the lower end of the screw was immersed in the water to be pumped and the water lifted to a height equal to the length of the cylinder multiplied by the sine of the angle of inclination to the horizontal.

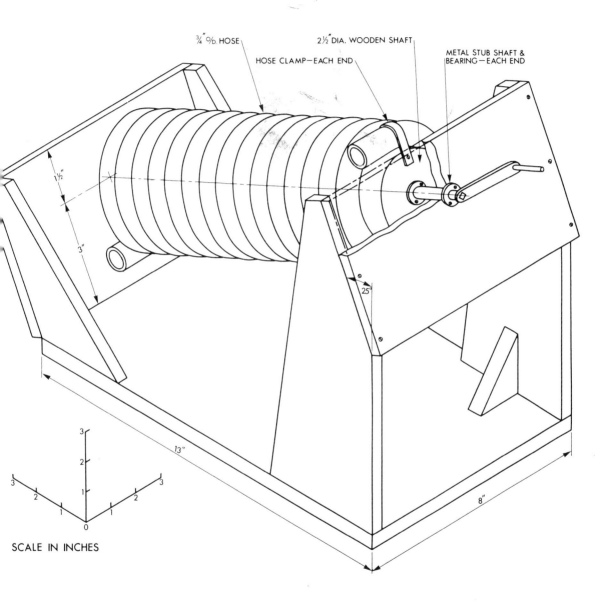

¾" o/p. HOSE

2½" DIA. WOODEN SHAFT

METAL STUB SHAFT &
BEARING—EACH END

HOSE CLAMP—EACH END

1½"

3"

25°

3
2
1
3   3
2   2
1   1
0

SCALE IN INCHES

13"

8"

Fig. 5/1   Archimedean snail

Tympanum

Another device for water raising used in Greek times was the Tympanum which was a compartmented drum of cylindrical or of octagonal cross-section divided into radial compartments, each of which had an inlet in the circumference and an outlet near to the axis. The drum was divided up into segments by radial partitions and the lower part of the perimeter was immersed in the water so that as the drum was rotated, a quantity of water contained in one of the radial sections was carried up above the water-level and the contents discharged through the outlet near the axis of the drum. A model of this apparatus which is turned by a hand crank is shown in Fig. 5/2. The full-scale machine would have been turned by the feet of a slave in the same way as the archimedean snail.

This apparatus was used only for smaller lifts and the net height through which the water was lifted could only be rather less than the radius of the drum.

It will be found in operating this model that there is an optimum speed of rotation which depends on the size of the inlets and outlets to the compartments. If the drum is rotated too fast, the compartments do not have time to fill and empty so that the maximum delivery is obtained with a comparatively slow rotation. A further interesting feature of the type illustrated is that it operates only when rotation is in the direction shown.

The model is constructed of $\frac{1}{8}$ in hardboard as shown in Fig. 5/2a. Before the outer boards are fixed during assembly the radial vanes and framing must be glued and lacquered to be quite waterproof. Finally, the two sides and the boards on the periphery must be similarly treated. The outlet pipe should be of brass or copper.

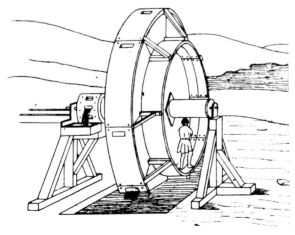

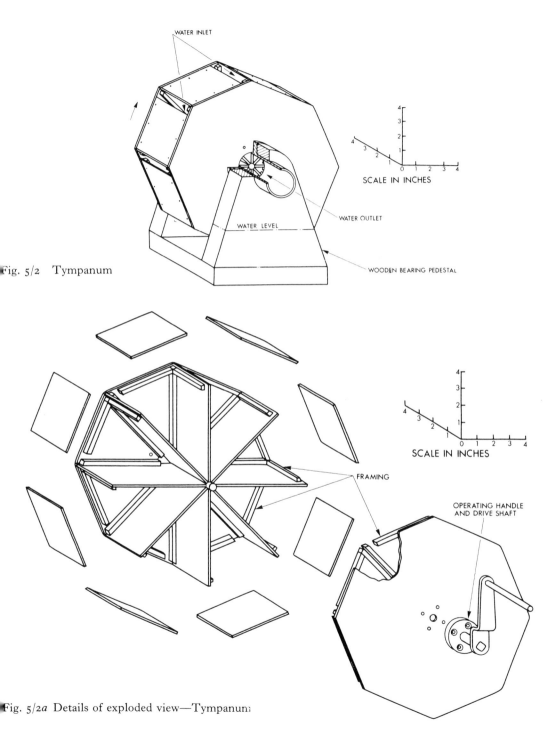

WATER INLET

SCALE IN INCHES

WATER OUTLET

WATER LEVEL

WOODEN BEARING PEDESTAL

Fig. 5/2   Tympanum

SCALE IN INCHES

FRAMING

OPERATING HANDLE
AND DRIVE SHAFT

Fig. 5/2a Details of exploded view—Tympanum

Ctesibian Pump

The Ctesibian pump, which is about two thousand years old, is the original type of force pump used for fire fighting and, like so many early machines, it was operated by a balance beam. In the models, the two hands of the operator are used to depress the two ends of the beam alternately. To each end of the beam is attached a piston moving up and down in a cylinder with sufficient clearance at the end of the piston rod to allow the piston to move vertically within a fixed vertical cylinder. The two cylinders of brass or copper are mounted on a wooden base, as are the delivery pipes and nozzles. The connecting pipes are 1 in diameter and the nozzle which is only $\frac{1}{8}$ in diameter is connected up in the manner shown in the drawing, Fig. 5/3a, so that a column of water can be projected from the nozzle in any direction by twisting it or the vertical pipe to which it is attached. The packing shown makes it possible to do this without leakage. The operating lever or beam which is hinged at its centre is 16 in long between the handles and is made of wood.

The most important features of the pump are the suction and delivery valves, the former are situated in a clear plastic valve-chest in the base of each cylinder and the latter in the branch pipes. Following the original design as closely as possible, the suction

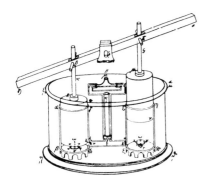

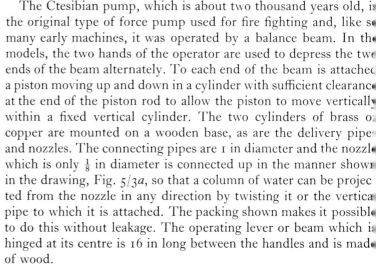

SCALE IN INCHES

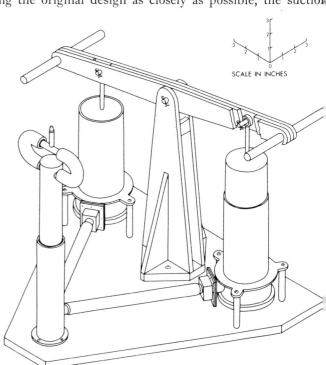

Fig. 5/3 Ctesibian force pump
—external view

alves are flat cylindrical discs of copper which are lifted off their
eats by the suction and returned by gravity. The delivery valves
re identical but mounted in the vertical plane.

It is important with this model that the water-level should be
high enough to drown the suction valves as it will not work as a
suction pump. Another important feature of this model is that the
valves should be of sufficient weight to close when immersed in
water.

Two drawings are given—one is an isometric outside view of the
complete pump, Fig. 5/3a—and the other a cross-section through
the cylinder and the delivery pipe, Fig. 5/3. The model is standing in
a shallow tank filled to the water-level shown.

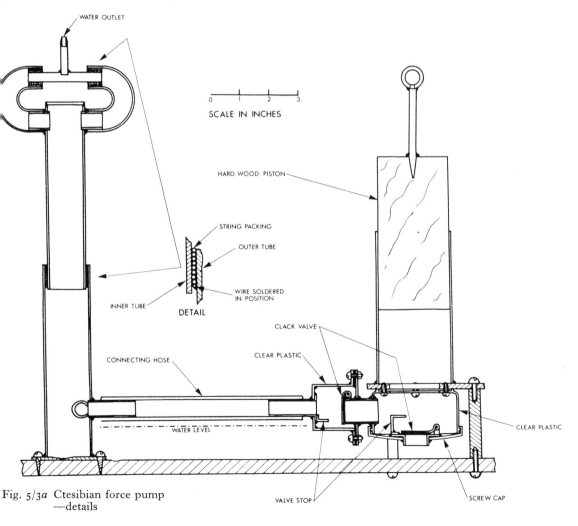

WATER OUTLET

SCALE IN INCHES
0   1   2   3

HARD WOOD PISTON

STRING PACKING

OUTER TUBE

WIRE SOLDERED
IN POSITION

INNER TUBE

DETAIL

CLACK VALVE

CONNECTING HOSE

CLEAR PLASTIC

CLEAR PLASTIC

WATER LEVEL

Fig. 5/3a Ctesibian force pump
—details

VALVE STOP

SCREW CAP

The Rag and Chain Pump

The rag and chain pump illustrated in Fig. 5/4 was described by Agricola in 1550 as his favourite pump for raising water and there is no doubt that it was in very general use throughout Europe and the Arabian world at that time.

It consists essentially of a wheel with a horizontal axis around which a chain is passed, the chain passing up through a vertical tube from a tank at the base and having balls of rag attached to it at equal intervals along its length. As the wheel is rotated the balls of rag are drawn up through the vertical tube and if the bottom of the tube dips into water, water will be pumped up through the tube as the wheel is turned. This is brought about by the temporary sealing of the vertical tube by the balls of rag which fit tightly in the tube and thus prevent the water from falling downwards. The upper end of the tube is open to the air and may be slotted at the top so as to allow the issuing water to emerge as freely as possible; the lower end should be bell-mounted to avoid the balls catching on entry. In the model illustrated the water is raised about 2 ft in height in a copper tube and by turning the horizontal wheel rapidly a large quantity of water can be pumped with it. When the model is operated, water is drawn up from the bucket below, discharged into the tray at the top, and flows back to the bucket through the return pipe.

In the Middle Ages the wheel was often turned by horses through crude gearing or by a treadmill containing the "tramping men".

The model is made principally of wood and hardboard which should be waterproofed as with the previous model.

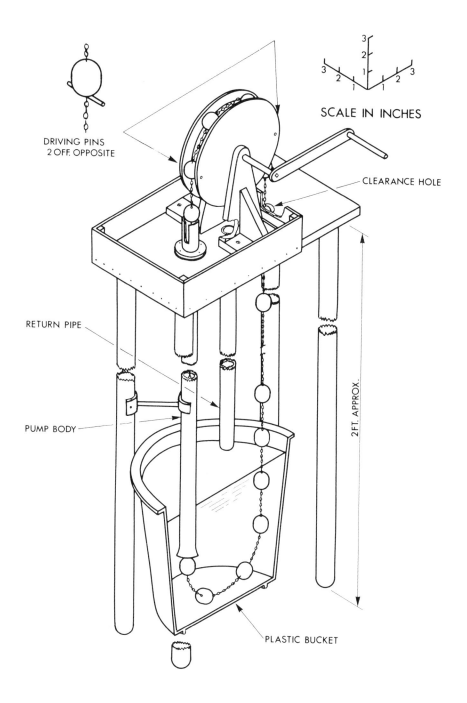

DRIVING PINS
2 OFF. OPPOSITE

3
2
3 1
3 2 1 1 2 3

SCALE IN INCHES

CLEARANCE HOLE

RETURN PIPE

2 FT. APPROX.

PUMP BODY

PLASTIC BUCKET

fig. 5/4   Rag and chain pump

The Suction Pump

An elegant model of the suction pump, the type that is still to be found on many a village green, can be made up of copper tubing preferably of three different diameters. The barrel portion in the model shown is 9 in long and the flap valves or clacks (Fig. 5/5a) are made of rubber sheet to which brass plate has been fixed with suitable adhesive. The piston is made from a standard cup-washer. The model shown stands on three legs over a plastic bucket as shown in the half-section drawing, Fig. 5/5.

The important feature of this pump which first came into use in the fourteenth century, is that it is capable of lifting water from the bottom of the well provided that the well is not more than 30 ft deep. If the pump is carefully made there is no need for priming and this can be demonstrated every time that the pump is first used after the bucket has been emptied, or by opening and then closing the vacuum release valve.

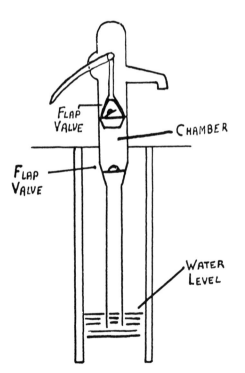

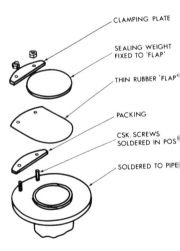

Fig. 5/5a Exploded view of non-return valve

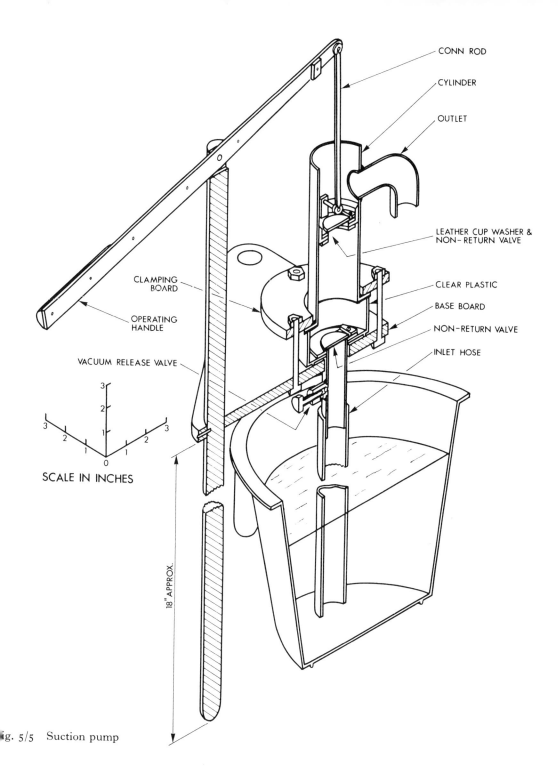

CONN ROD

CYLINDER

OUTLET

LEATHER CUP WASHER &
NON-RETURN VALVE

CLEAR PLASTIC

BASE BOARD

NON-RETURN VALVE

INLET HOSE

CLAMPING
BOARD

OPERATING
HANDLE

VACUUM RELEASE VALVE

3
2
1
3   3
2   2
1   0   1

SCALE IN INCHES

18" APPROX.

Fig. 5/5   Suction pump

The Cow Pump

A very simple arrangement for pumping water, known as the *cow pump*, is coming into general use in cases where sterility of the water or fluid being pumped is of great importance.

The writer's model, Fig. 5/6, has $\frac{1}{2}$ in rubber tubing and four rollers. Two tanks are needed, one for the suction and one for delivery. The flow can be reversed by reversing the direction of rotation. No valves are needed since their function is performed by the pinching of the rubber tube between the rollers and the enclosing arc of wood.

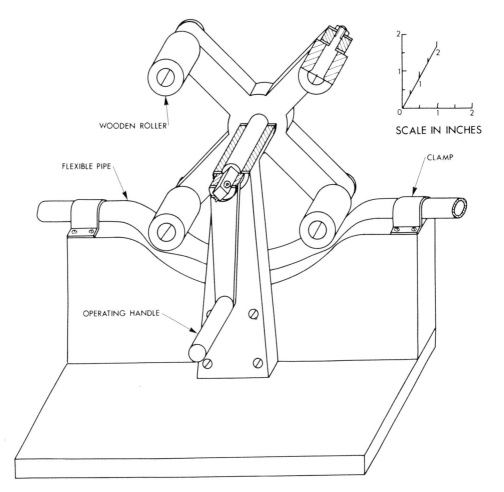

SCALE IN INCHES

WOODEN ROLLER

FLEXIBLE PIPE

CLAMP

OPERATING HANDLE

Fig. 5/6   Cow pump

The Diaphragm Pump

A type of pump that is particularly suitable for pumping small quantities of fluids is the *diaphragm pump*, now familiar in a miniature form, as the standard petrol pump on most automobiles. It was first used for pumping water—about two hundred years ago. The model shown in half-section, Fig. 5/7, is mounted on a wooden base-board which can be placed directly on top of a plastic bucket.

The modern petrol pump with its metal diaphragm and minute valves—works very fast and for long periods without any attention.

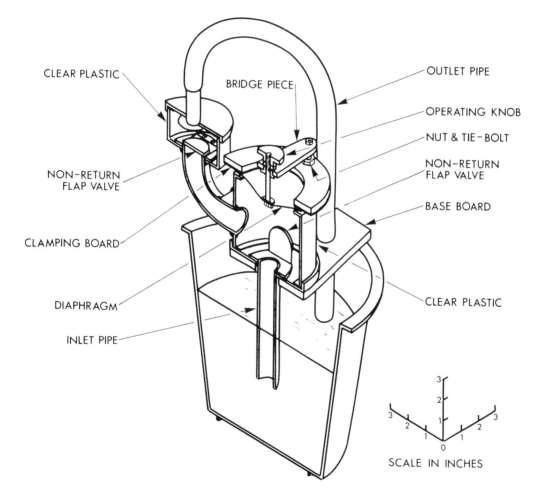

CLEAR PLASTIC

BRIDGE PIECE

OUTLET PIPE

OPERATING KNOB

NUT & TIE-BOLT

NON-RETURN FLAP VALVE

NON-RETURN FLAP VALVE

BASE BOARD

CLAMPING BOARD

DIAPHRAGM

INLET PIPE

CLEAR PLASTIC

SCALE IN INCHES

Fig. 5/7   Diaphragm pump

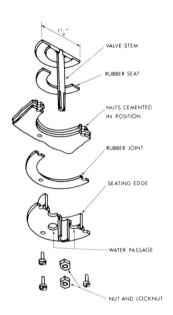

VALVE STEM

RUBBER SEAT

NUTS CEMENTED
IN POSITION

RUBBER JOINT

SEATING EDGE

WATER PASSAGE

NUT AND LOCKNUT

Fig. 5/8*b* Exploded view of valve
—hydraulic ram

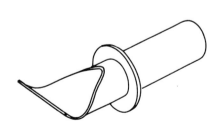

Fig. 5/8*c* View of inlet pipe
—hydraulic ram

The Hydraulic Ram

One of the most interesting working models that can be made by the amateur is the hydraulic ram first invented by Montgolfier in 1797 and still used as a means for pumping water in country houses, provided that a continuous supply of water from a stream or brook is available to operate the apparatus. The essential part is a rectangular chamber containing a delivery valve and a spill valve, which will each operate automatically by the water supply once the device has been started. The model shown, Fig. 5/8, has light poppet valves made of brass, each mounted with its axis vertical in the lid of a box made of plastic material, such as a lunch box for carrying sandwiches (see Fig. 5/8*a*). The box being made of transparent plastic, enables the operation of the valves to be seen clearly and of all the models described here this one is probably the most impressive and exciting to those who are unfamiliar with hydraulics.

In the model, the water wasted which passes out through the spill valve on the right is about one quarter of the quantity pumped up through the delivery valve. The air chamber ensures a steady even flow of the delivery in spite of the intermittent flow through the valves. As illustrated, in Fig. 5/8, the upper header tank is 12 in above the receiver tank but the water can be pumped to a very much greater height if it is convenient or necessary to do so. The hydraulic ram will continue to operate by itself without any attention so long as the water supply in the top tank is maintained so that when it is used on remote farms it can be relied upon to continue to operate almost indefinitely with very little maintenance. The only moving parts are the two valves which are lubricated by the water supply.

In constructing this apparatus it is absolutely essential that there should be no leaks in the air chamber and water-box. In the half section drawing of the ram assembly, Fig. 5/8*a*, the places that have been glued with suitable adhesive (Araldite) have been shown in section as dark segments. The two valves are identical in construction (see Fig. 5/8*b*).

The hydraulic ram depends for its functioning on the wave action set up in the water-box by the closing alternately of the two valves. As each valve closes, a wave is reflected from it through the water in the box until it meets the other valve which thereupon opens, and when the wave energy has been dispersed, the valve closes causing another wave to be reflected in the opposite direction. This alternating flow will continue indefinitely provided that the lift of the two valves has been appropriately adjusted in the first place. Adjustment can be done by trial and error and when the right lift has been found the two nuts must be locked in position on each valve spindle.

To start the ram working one has only to depress the spill valve momentarily. To stop it, the spill valve is held against its seat, where it will remain stationary until depressed again.

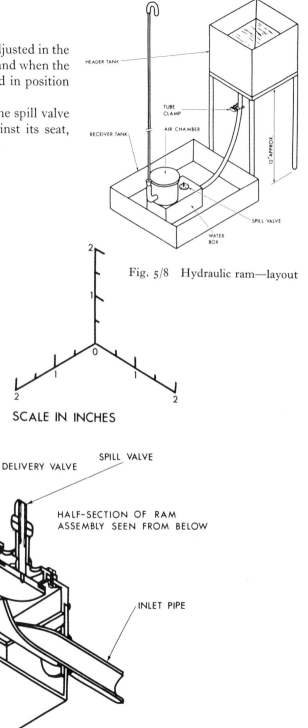

Fig. 5/8 Hydraulic ram—layout

SCALE IN INCHES

Fig. 5/8a Half-section of ram assembly

Chapter VI Blowing Machines

The Valveless Bellows

Throughout the ages many different varieties of equipment have been used for blowing air. Some means of blowing air has always been required, principally for the purpose of smelting metals in fires of charcoal or fossil fuel (coal). Primitive peoples have been depicted blowing up their fires for smelting metals by using a mouth blowpipe, and indeed this was done, though such a method is only suitable for obtaining an extremely high temperature in a very small fire, for example, for smelting gold. For many kindred purposes and also for other uses, such as ventilation, a machine that will blow large quantities of air while raising it to a comparatively small pressure is required.

The reader may wonder why leathern bellows or the piston type of blower, such as a bicycle pump, have not been included in place of the blowers illustrated. There are several reasons for this; in the first place both are difficult to manufacture and secondly neither of them gives a steady even continuous blast of air, as the flow has to be interrupted while the operator makes the return stroke. The two blowers illustrated here do not suffer from these defects. Futhermore, many readers will not have come across them before and both are of great historical interest. The first has been termed the valveless bellows and is of such ancient origin that no one can say when it was first made. It consists of two circular wooden bowls placed side by side, each covered at the top with leather or skin to which a handle is attached. In its original form these might well be animal skins with a leg bone near the centre which could be grasped by the operator. The outer edges of the skins were fastened to the rims of the bowls by tying the skins on with leather thongs. Near the bottom of each bowl, a small pipe was attached and these two pipes were brought together as shown in the picture, Fig. 6/1, at the entrance of a nozzle pipe or *tuyere*, the far end of which projected into the fire. The operator held one handle in each hand and raised and lowered them alternately thus creating a steady draught into the fire. Notice that when each handle is raised, air into that dish is sucked in at the large end of the tuyere at the same time that air is being blown into the fire from the other bowl.

The tuyere should be made of fireclay since its small end is immersed in the fire. Two fire bricks to contain the fire are shown resting on the table which is covered with fire bricks.

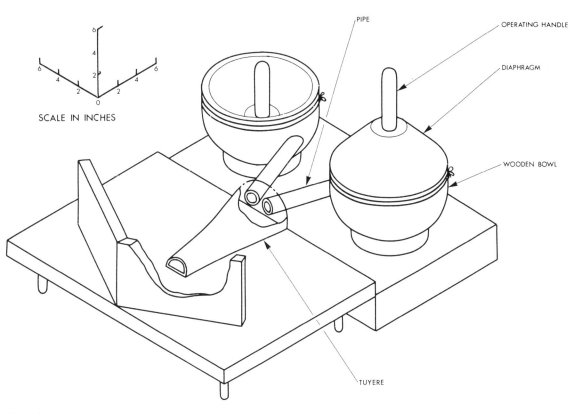

Fig. 6/1 Valveless bellows

Modern primitive valveless bellows as used for smelting iron in the Sudan

The Chinese Double-acting Blower

The second blowing machine illustrated in Fig. 6/2 is the Chinese double-acting blower. This is more than two thousand years old but was still in use in China at the beginning of this century. It is thought by many to be the first double-acting machine, that is to say, that both sides of the moving piston are used for blowing the air. Accordingly, the chambers at each end of the box have to be provided with valves.

The model shown has two inlet valves at each end, the valves are leather flaps, stiffened with wood, the pistons and piston-rods are not circular in section but square or rectangular and, instead of providing a separate delivery valve for the air coming from each side of the piston, the Chinese designer of this apparatus very ingeniously arranged a flap valve which operated first for one side and then for the other so that the single flap valve served as a delivery valve for each compartment of the blower.

The outlet pipe through which the air issues from the blower to the fire, or other apparatus where it is required, is at the back of the main drawing and is shown in a separate sketch at the side. To maintain a seal between the compartments on either side of the piston, the piston itself is packed with down or chicken's feathers.

The front side of the piston chamber and of the air passages immediately below it may be faced with a sheet of glass or plastic ($\frac{1}{8}$ in thick) so that the movement of the piston and inlet valves may be seen. The two-way delivery valve can be faced similarly with transparent material.

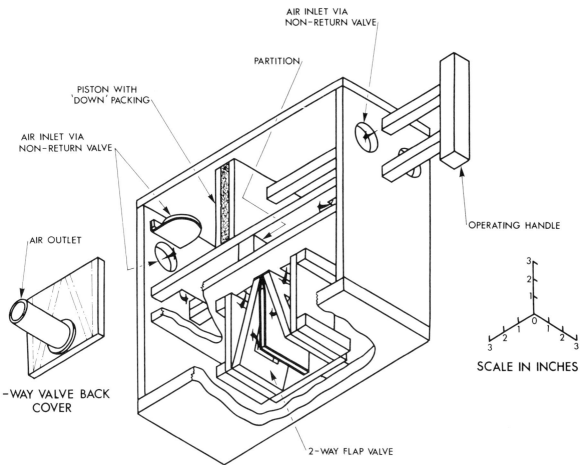

AIR INLET VIA
NON-RETURN VALVE

PARTITION

PISTON WITH
'DOWN' PACKING

AIR INLET VIA
NON-RETURN VALVE

AIR OUTLET

OPERATING HANDLE

3
2
1
0
1 2
3
3 2 1 2 3

SCALE IN INCHES

-WAY VALVE BACK
COVER

2-WAY FLAP VALVE

Fig. 6/2   Chinese double-acting blower

Chapter VII   Heat Engines

Temple Doors

Two distinctly different types of heat engines were known to the Greeks two thousand years ago, though the principles upon which they operated were not understood until some hundreds of years later. The first of these was the device used for the automatic opening of the doors of the temple before a sacrifice was burned on the altar, and for reopening the doors when the sacrifice was consumed.

In its original form the altar was constructed of copper sheet and the upper surface was recessed to contain the fire. Around the fire was an air space, completely sealed off so that when the fire was lighted on the altar top the air contained in the space below was heated and therefore expanded. The air then passed down through the floor of the temple into a sealed jar in the room below where it displaced water (shown in the bottle in the sketch). This water was forced out of the vessel which contained it through a syphon pipe into a bucket. As the bucket became heavier due to filling with water its weight became greater than that of counterweights which were holding the doors in position and so the doors closed. Since the bucket was attached by cords to the spindles of the doors, as the buckets moved downwards, the spindles rotated to close the doors.

When the ceremony was over the reverse process took place and this involved the syphoning of the water out of the bucket by the slight vacuum created in the air space in the altar and the receiver below it. As the pressure in the air vessel around the altar decreased due to the cooling of the fire, the slight vacuum sucked the water out of the bucket into the vessel, so the weight of the bucket grew less and the counterweights then opened the doors of the temple allowing the congregation to disperse.

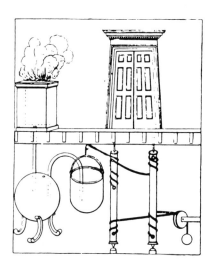

The model of this apparatus, shown in Fig. 7/1, consists largely of wood; the doors, the floor of the temple and the casing of the altar can all be made of wood. Some metal parts are needed for the spindle ends of the doors and the altar shelf and its surrounds. Glass or plastic bottles are needed for containing the water. A special feature of the model (added for demonstration and not part of the original device) is a cold-water-jacket enabling the altar to be cooled down fairly rapidly to demonstrate the opening of the doors at the end of the ceremony.

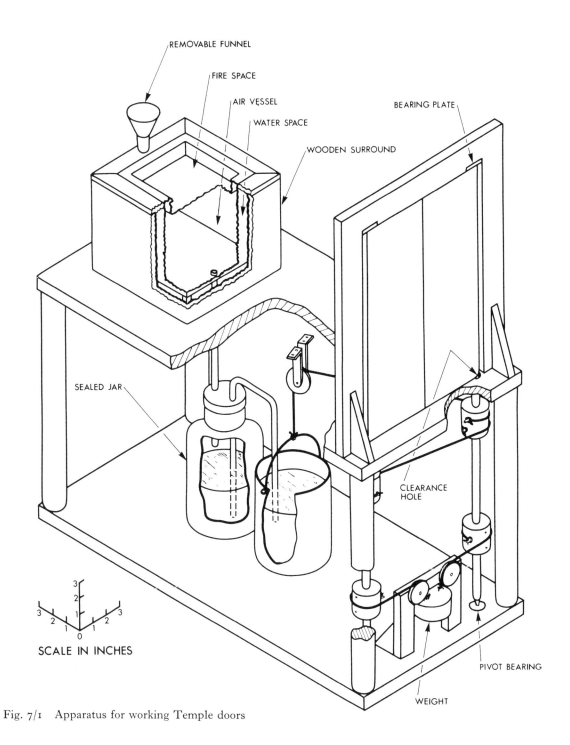

REMOVABLE FUNNEL

FIRE SPACE

AIR VESSEL

WATER SPACE

WOODEN SURROUND

BEARING PLATE

SEALED JAR

CLEARANCE HOLE

PIVOT BEARING

WEIGHT

SCALE IN INCHES

3
2
1
3 2 1   1 2 3
0

Fig. 7/1   Apparatus for working Temple doors

Hero's Whirling Aeolipile

Another ancient heat engine of which a model can be made quite conveniently is Hero's Whirling Aeolipile. It was the first *reaction steam turbine* and was described by Hero in the first century A.D. It was used only as a toy to entertain admiring guests at dinner in Roman times. The apparatus was no larger than that shown in the sketch and the original form of the water container was spherical and not cylindrical as shown here; the cylindrical form has been adopted for this model because it is so much easier for the amateur to manufacture. Indeed, the main water container, or cylinder, can be made out of a tin-can provided that it is watertight and will stand the temperature of boiling water.

As can be seen on the sketch, Fig. 7/2, the water container rotates about a horizontal axis. As soon as sufficient steam has been generated it is forced through the two nozzles causing a reaction which turns the cylinder so that it whirls round in quite a spectacular fashion, steam issuing from the two jets all the time. It is important that the apparatus should be in perfect balance and that it should rotate with the minimum amount of friction. Accordingly, it is essential that the two nozzle pipes should be the same length and weight, and positioned exactly opposite each other and the filling plug should be balanced by a similar weight being fixed to the opposite side of the drum. The nozzle pipes should extend well into the drum so that their inner extremities are near the axle. The reason for this is that as the apparatus whirls around, the water inside is thrown outwards and forms a layer on the inside surface of the drum. Thus, when the pipes are made to extend inwards to somewhere near the centre, steam alone (without water), issues out through the nozzles.

It may seen remarkable to people of this generation that such a very long time elapsed between the invention of this device, as a toy for amusement, and the invention of a practical reaction steam turbine that could be useful for industrial purposes. This latter event occurred only in 1884, when Sir Charles Parsons produced his first reaction steam turbine, whereas Hero's Aeolipile was certainly known seventeen hundred years before. Parsons himself, and others experimented in the last century with whirling-arm steam turbines and a few were built though they had a very restricted application; for example, de Laval in Sweden used the device to drive his well-known cream separator as it was the only means available to him for achieving the very high centrifugal speeds that he required for separating cream from milk.

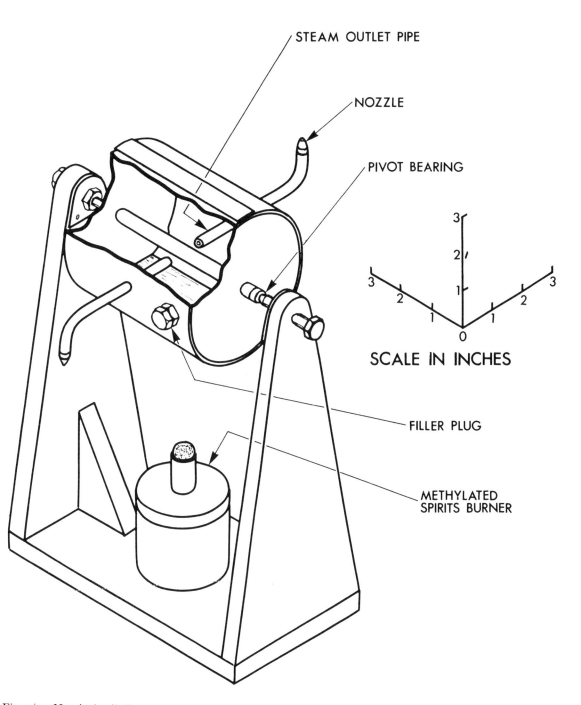

STEAM OUTLET PIPE

NOZZLE

PIVOT BEARING

3
2
1
3
2
1
0
1
1
2
2
3
3

SCALE IN INCHES

FILLER PLUG

METHYLATED
SPIRITS BURNER

Fig. 7/2   Hero's Aeolipile